Published by:

SQUIDWARD
An Imprint of
BLACKSPINE®

Blackspine Publishing Private Limited
Head Office: B-143, Ground Floor, Sector 6, Noida, UP, NCR, 201301
Regd. Office: 303/25 Eastend, Mayur Vihar Phase-1, Delhi-110096
Phone: 98102-28588
E-mail: info@blackspinepublishing.com
Website: www.blackspinepublishing.com

Conquer Pre-School Mathematics LKG- B

ISBN-13 **978-93-89219-16-6**

Indian Edition 2024

Printed in India

Our Global Partners' Network:

Antigua & Barbuda
Australia
Bahrain
Bangladesh
Barbados
Bhutan
Botswana
Brazil
Brunei
Cambodia
Canada
Chile
China
Colombia
Egypt
Fiji
Ghana
Grenada
Guyana
India
Indonesia
Jamaica
Japan
Kenya
Laos
Lebanon
Malawi
Malaysia
Maldives
Mauritius
Myanmar
Namibia
Nepal
Netherlands
New Zealand
Nigeria
Pakistan
Papua New Guinea
Peru
Philippines
Poland
Portugal
Qatar
Rwanda
Saint Lucia
Saint Vincent & the Grenadines
Saudi Arabia
Seychelles
Singapore
Solomon Islands
South Africa
South Korea
Sri Lanka
Syria
Tanzania
Thailand
Trinidad & Tobago
United Arab Emirates
United Kingdom
United States of America
Vietnam
Zambia
Zimbabwe

For international business enquiries, email info@blackspinepublishing.com

PREFACE

Conquer Pre-school Mathematics is a pre-school series designed to prepare children for primary school. Each book, LKG-A, LKG-B, UKG-A and UKG-B, contains a careful selection of mathematical activities covering essential topics and skill sets.

"Let's start!"

Begin by downloading the FREE learning charts (blackspine.delhi@gmail.com) to complement the activities in the book. The charts serve as great learning and teaching tools.

"What's in this book?"

This pre-school series focuses on counting, addition and subtraction, and essential topics on measurements such as length, mass, time and money. The system of awarding marks for every activity is used to motivate the child in this learning adventure.

"Yes, I understand now!"

That's what we want to hear from the children when they try the activities in the book. The progressive activities are structured with specific learning objectives. Parents and educators will understand the purpose of each activity and they can monitor the children's progress and accomplishments.

Conquer Pre-school Mathematics LKG and **UKG** complete the learning of pre-school mathematics and prepare children for primary level mathematics.

The Editorial Team

CONTENTS

Learn these in Conquer Pre-School Mathematics K1A:

• Counting numbers 1-3 • Counting numbers 4-6 • Counting numbers 7-10 • Writing numbers in words • Counting numbers 1-10 • Adding up to 5 with pictures • Adding up to 10 with pictures • Adding using "more than" • Adding with pictures • Addition up to 10 • Subtraction with pictures within 10 • Subtracting using "less than" • Subtracting with pictures • Addition within 10 • Subtraction within 10 • Ordinal numbers • Identifying positions with pictures

ACTIVITY 24

Name ....
Class .... Date ....

/8 marks

1 Colour the watermelon **green**. Colour its flesh **red**.

2 Colour the papaya **orange**. Colour its seeds **black**.

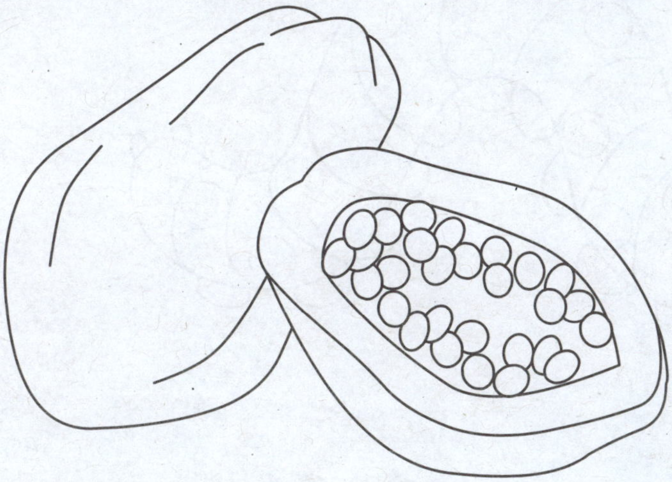

Learning Objective

Know and recognise colours

3 Colour the ladybird **red**. Colour its spots **black**.

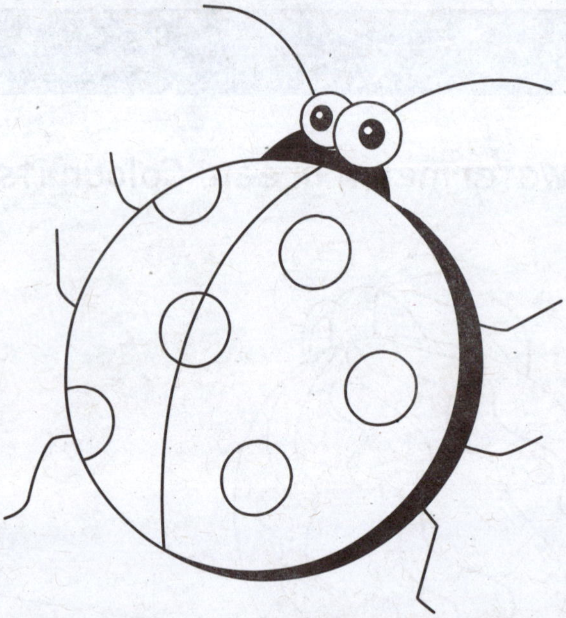

4 Colour the caterpillar **green**. Colour its spots **yellow**.

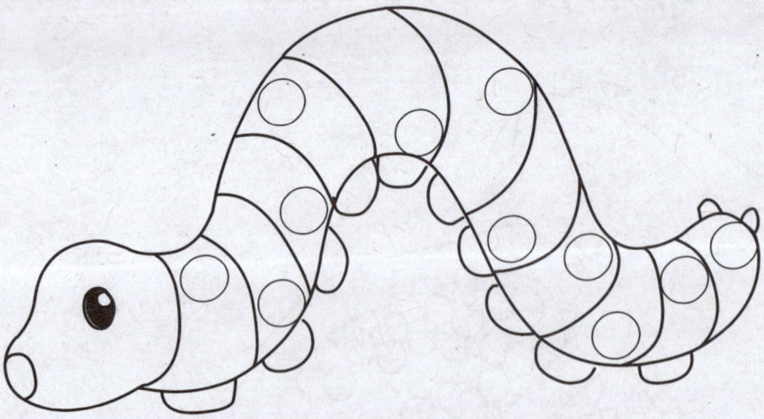

Learning Objective

Know and recognise colours

5 Colour the houses **blue**. Colour the roofs **brown**.

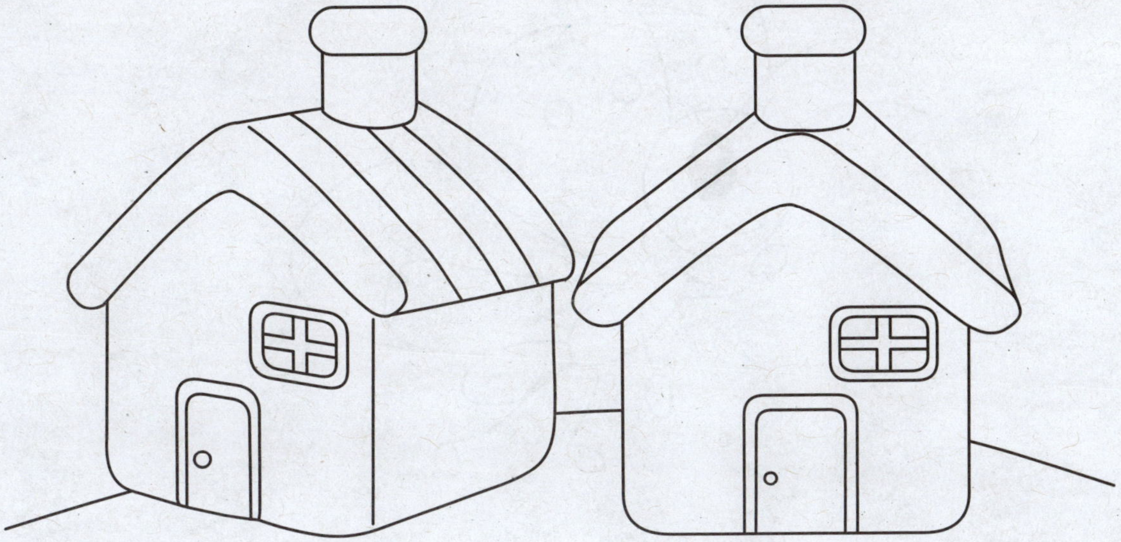

6 Colour the grapes **purple**. Colour the leaf **green**.

Learning Objective

Know and recognise colours

7 Colour the butterfly using **red**, **blue** and **black**.

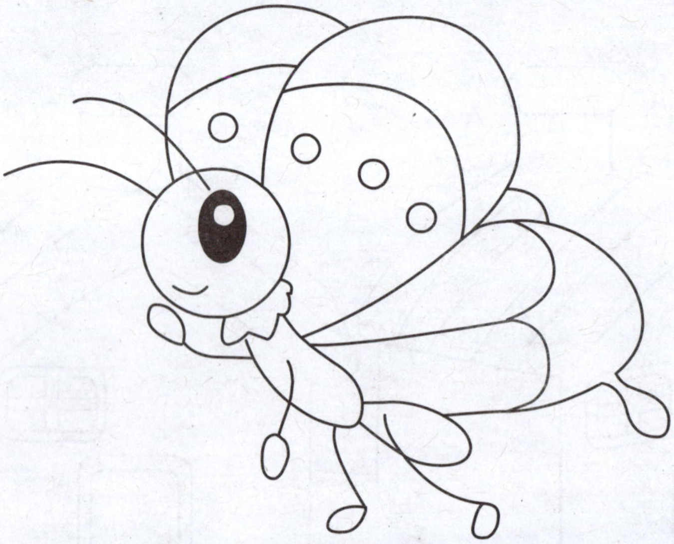

8 Colour the flower **red**. Colour its leaves **green**.

Learning Objective

Know and recognise colours

ACTIVITY 25

Name ....

Class .... Date ....

/10 marks

1 Rectangle

These things have the same shape as the rectangle.
Trace along the dotted lines.

Learning Objective

Know and recognise shapes

2 Square

These things have the same shape as the square.
Trace along the dotted lines.

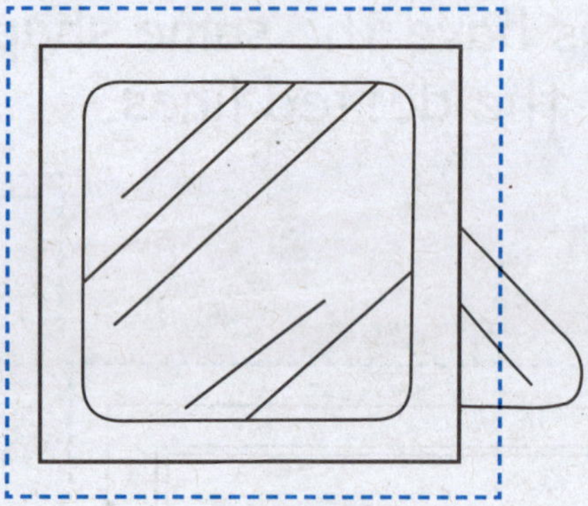

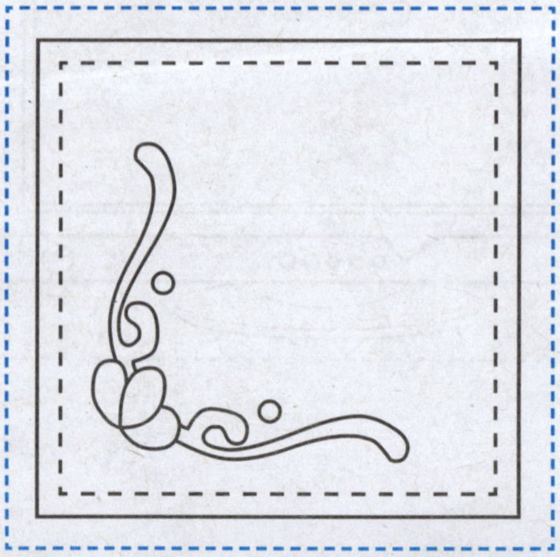

Learning Objective

Know and recognise shapes

3 Circle

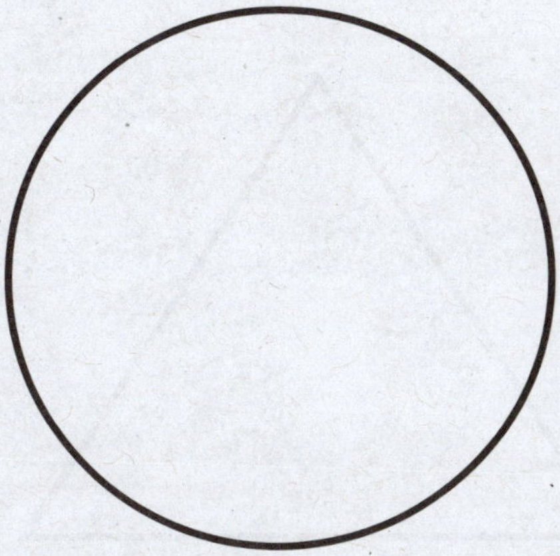

These things have the same shape as the circle.
Trace along the dotted lines.

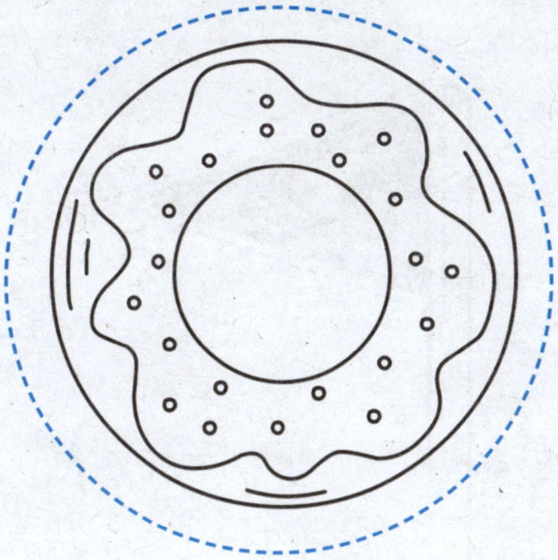

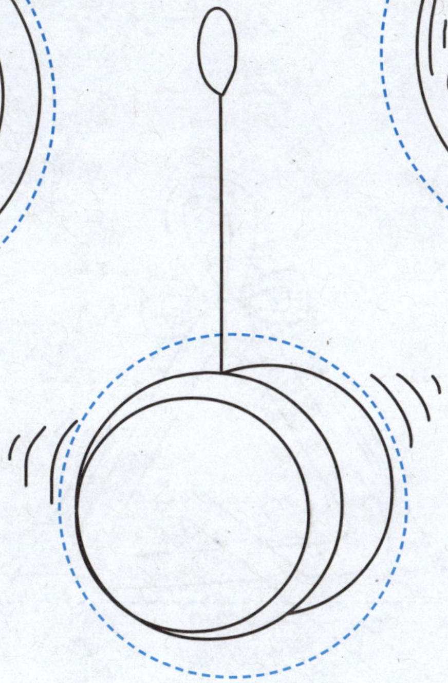

Learning Objective

Know and recognise shapes

4 Triangle

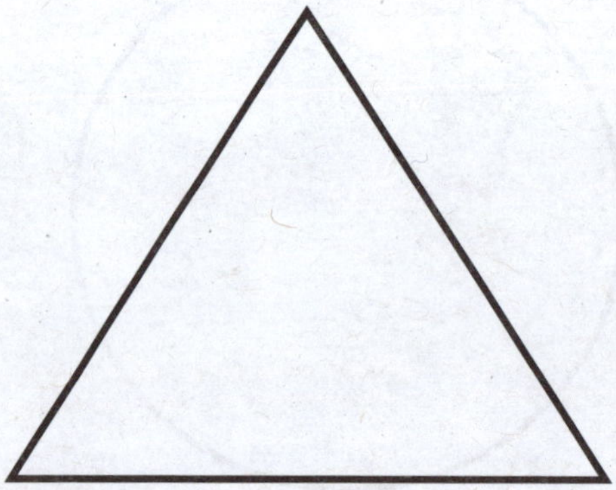

These things have the same shape as the triangle.
Trace along the dotted lines.

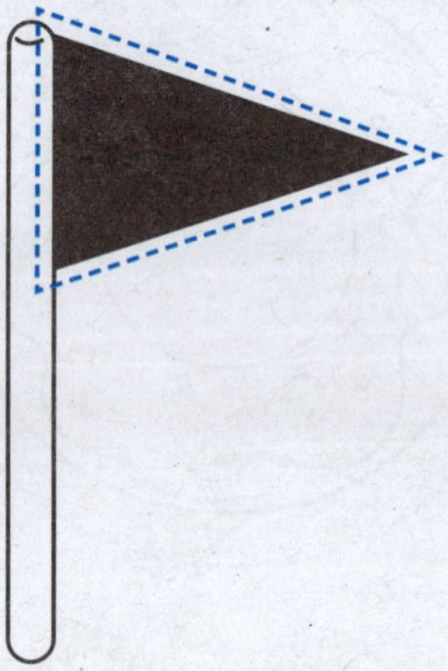

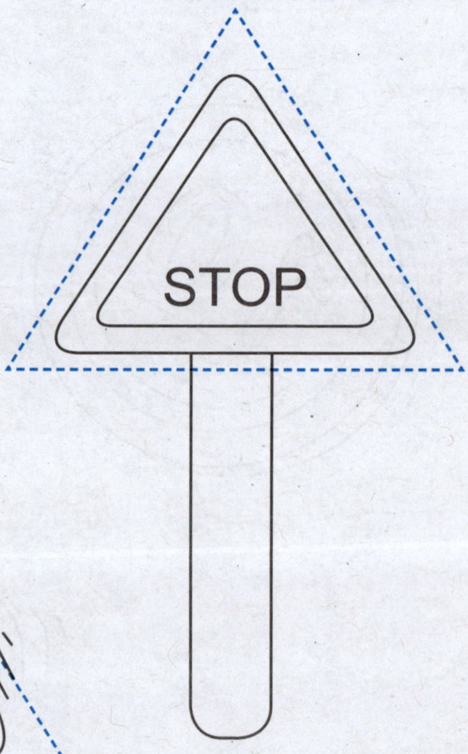

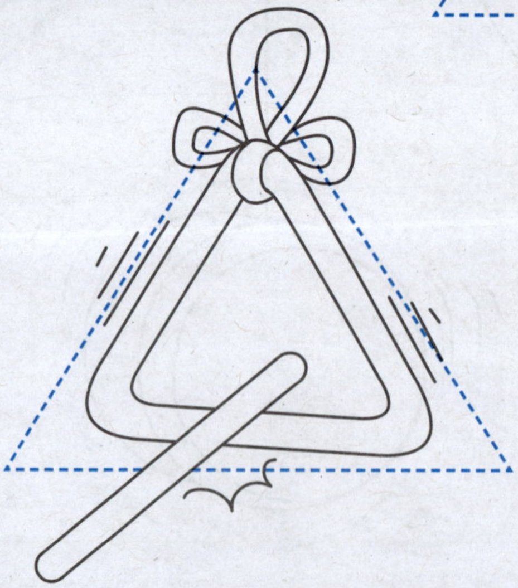

Learning Objective

Know and recognise shapes

5 Diamond

These things have the same shape as the diamond.
Trace along the dotted lines.

Learning Objective

Know and recognise shapes

6 Oval

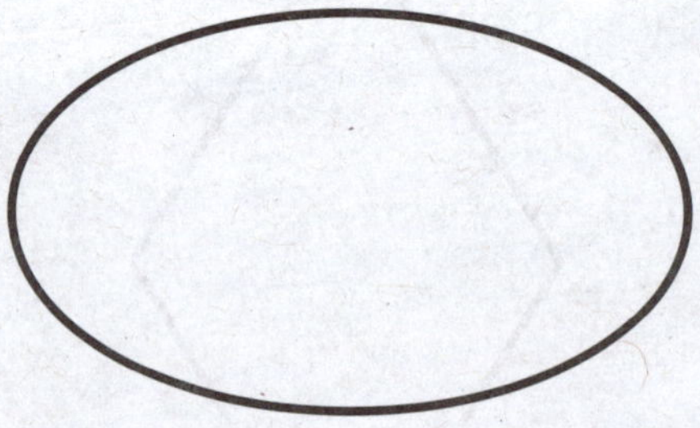

These things have the same shape as the oval.
Trace along the dotted lines.

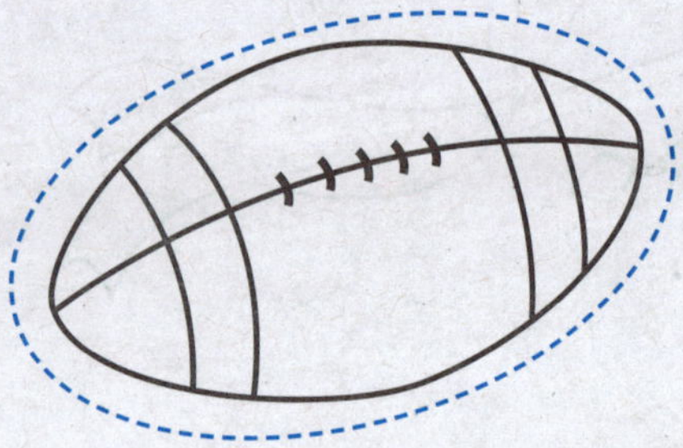

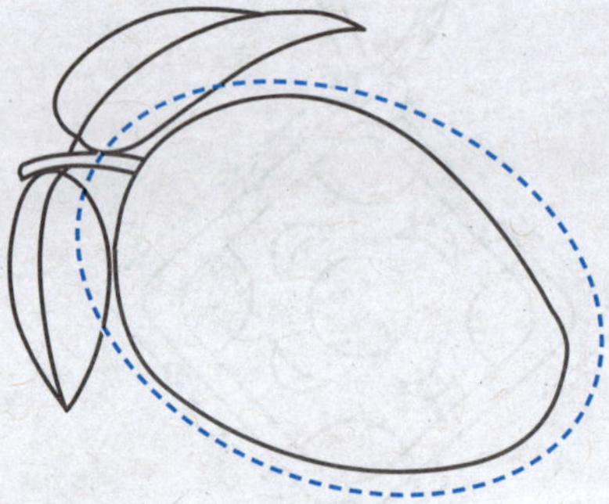

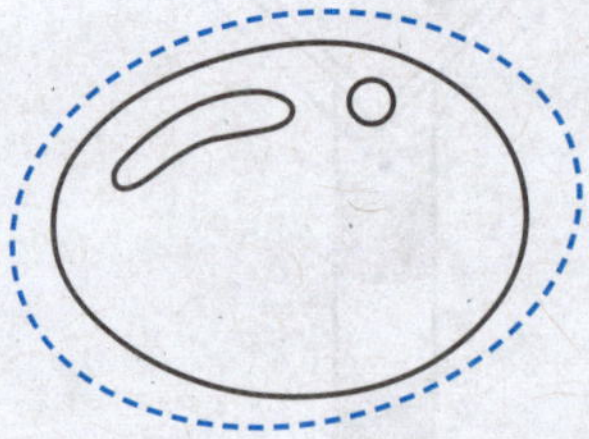

Learning Objective

Know and recognise shapes

7 Star

These things have the same shape as the star.
Trace along the dotted lines.

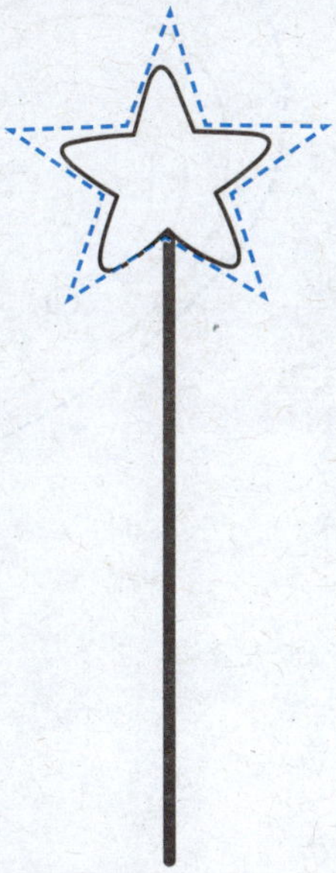

Learning Objective

Know and recognise shapes

8 Heart

These things have the same shape as the heart.
Trace along the dotted lines.

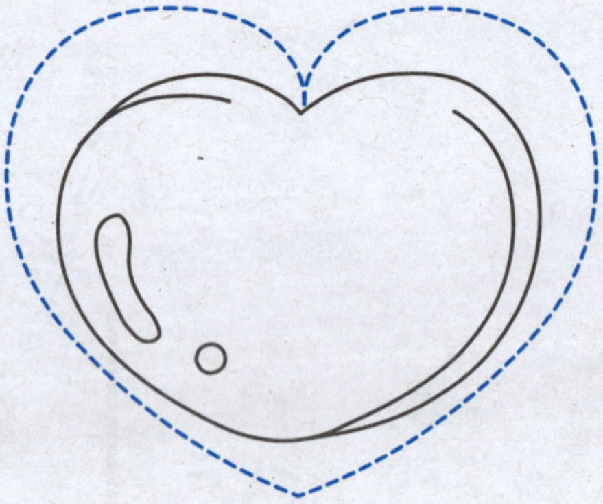

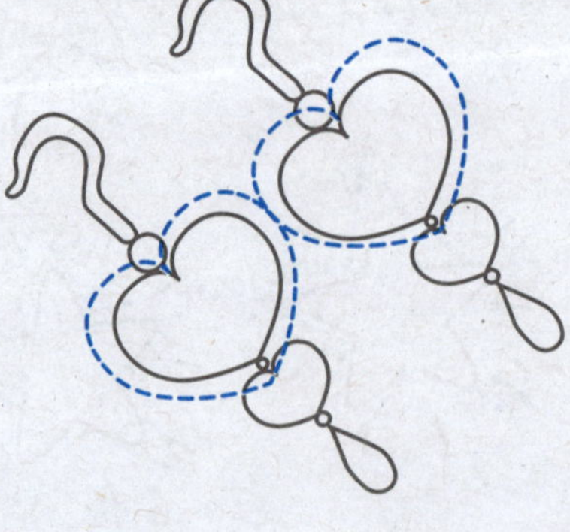

Learning Objective

Know and recognise shapes

9 Crescent

These things have the same shape as the crescent.
Trace along the dotted lines.

Learning Objective

Know and recognise shapes

10 Cone

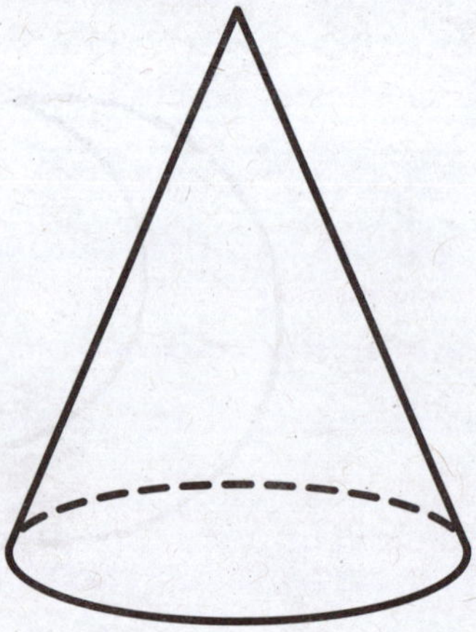

These things have the same shape as the cone.
Trace along the dotted lines.

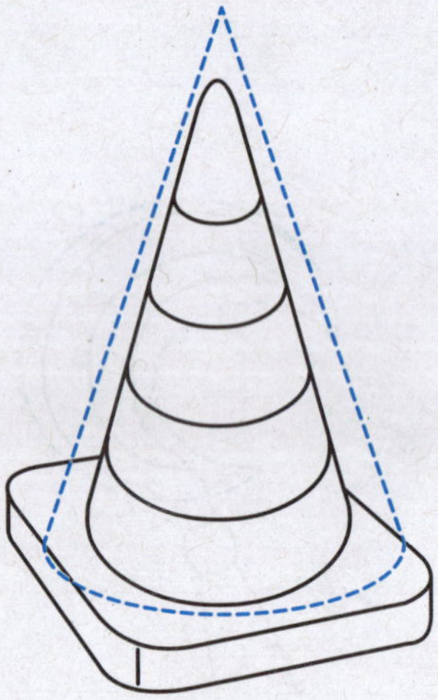

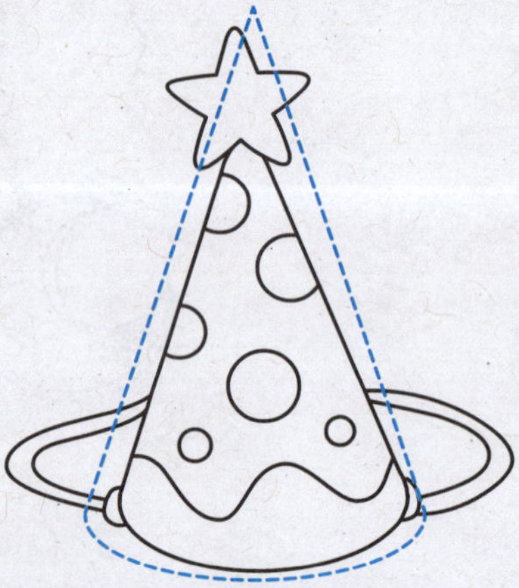

Learning Objective

Know and recognise shapes

ACTIVITY 26

Name ....

Class .... Date ....

/ 8 marks

1 Colour all the **rectangles** red.

Learning Objective

Identifying colours and shapes

2 Cross out all the **squares** using a blue coloured pencil.

Learning Objective

Identifying colours and shapes

3 Circle all the **triangles**.

Learning Objective

Identifying colours and shapes

4 Colour all the **ovals** yellow.

Learning Objective

Identifying colours and shapes

5 Cross out all the circles using a black coloured pencil.

6 Circle all the **diamonds**.

Learning Objective

Identifying colours and shapes

7 Draw a tick (☒) on all the **stars** using a green coloured pencil.

Learning Objective

Identifying colours and shapes

8 Colour all the **crescents** brown.

Learning Objective

Identifying colours and shapes

ACTIVITY 27

Name ....

Class .... Date ....

/10 marks

Count and write the correct number on each line.

1 There are ____________ circles ○.

2 There are ____________ triangles △.

3 There are ____________ rectangles ▭.

4 There are ____________ ovals ⬭.

5 There are ____________ squares □.

6 There are ____________ crescents ☾.

Learning Objective

Counting shapes

Count and write the correct number on each line.

7 There are ______________ stars ☆.

8 There are ______________ hearts ♡.

9 There are ______________ diamonds ◇.

10 There are ______________ cones.

Learning Objective

Counting shapes

ACTIVITY 28

Name .... Class .... Date .... /8 marks

1 Colour the **bigger** spider.

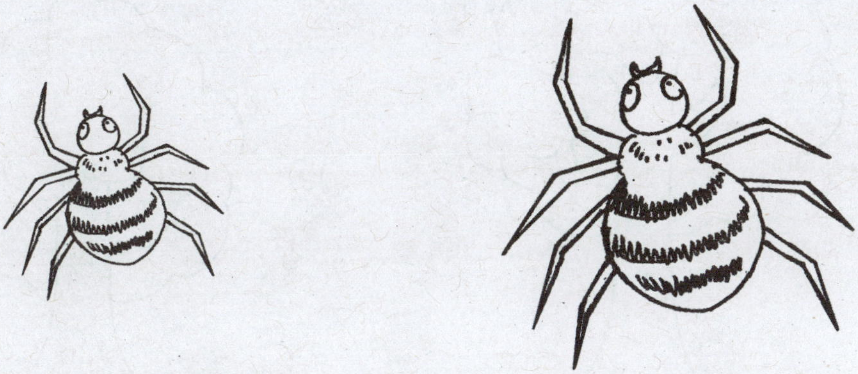

2 Colour the **smaller** mouse.

Learning Objective

Exploring measurements

3 Circle the taller tree.

taller shorter

4 Circle the shorter boy.

taller shorter

5 Colour the **taller** house.

6 Colour the **shorter** plant.

Learning Objective

Exploring measurements

7 Colour the **taller** giraffe.

8 Colour the **shorter** tree.

Learning Objective

Exploring measurements

ACTIVITY 29

Name .... Class .... Date .... /10 marks

Circle the correct object.

1 taller

2 shorter

Learning Objective

Understanding length

3 Colour the longer ruler.

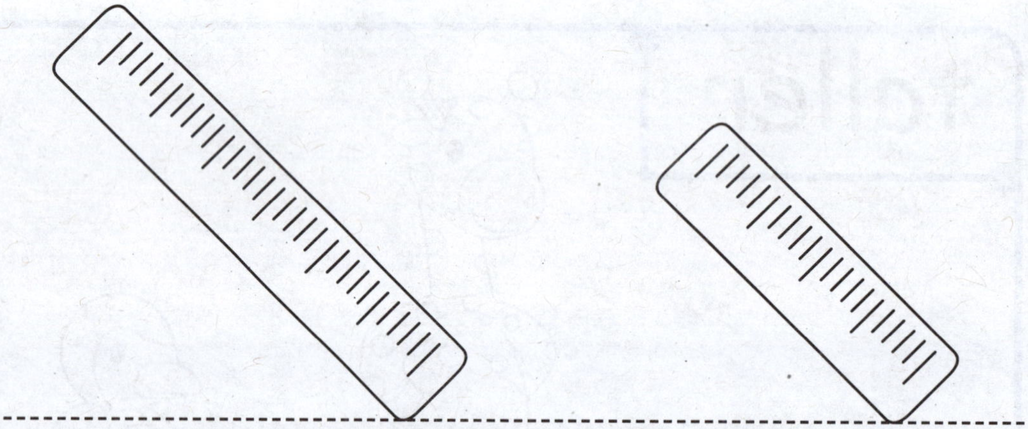

4 Colour the shorter pencil.

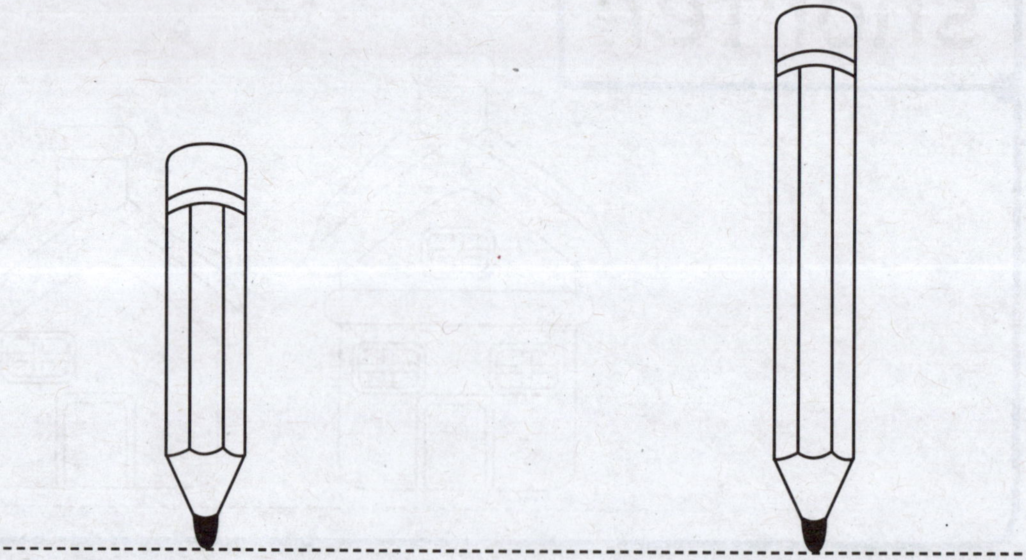

Learning Objective

Understanding length

5 Draw a **longer** worm than the one below.

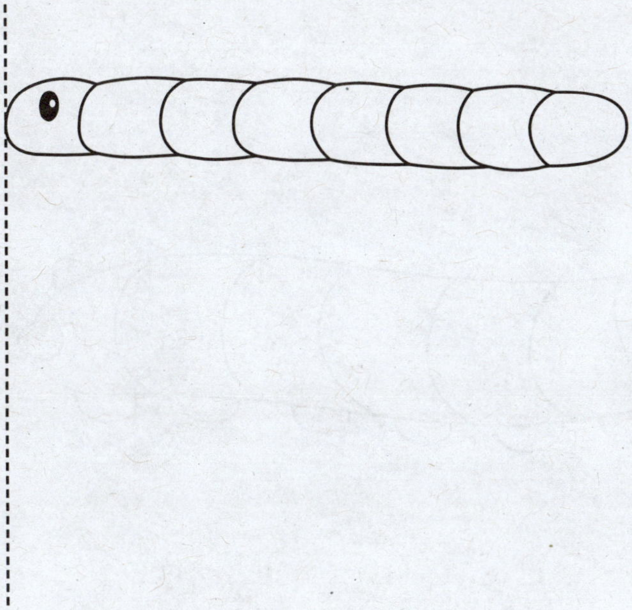

6 Draw a **shorter** pen than the one below.

Learning Objective

Understanding length

7 Colour the **longer** caterpillar green.
Colour the **shorter** caterpillar yellow.

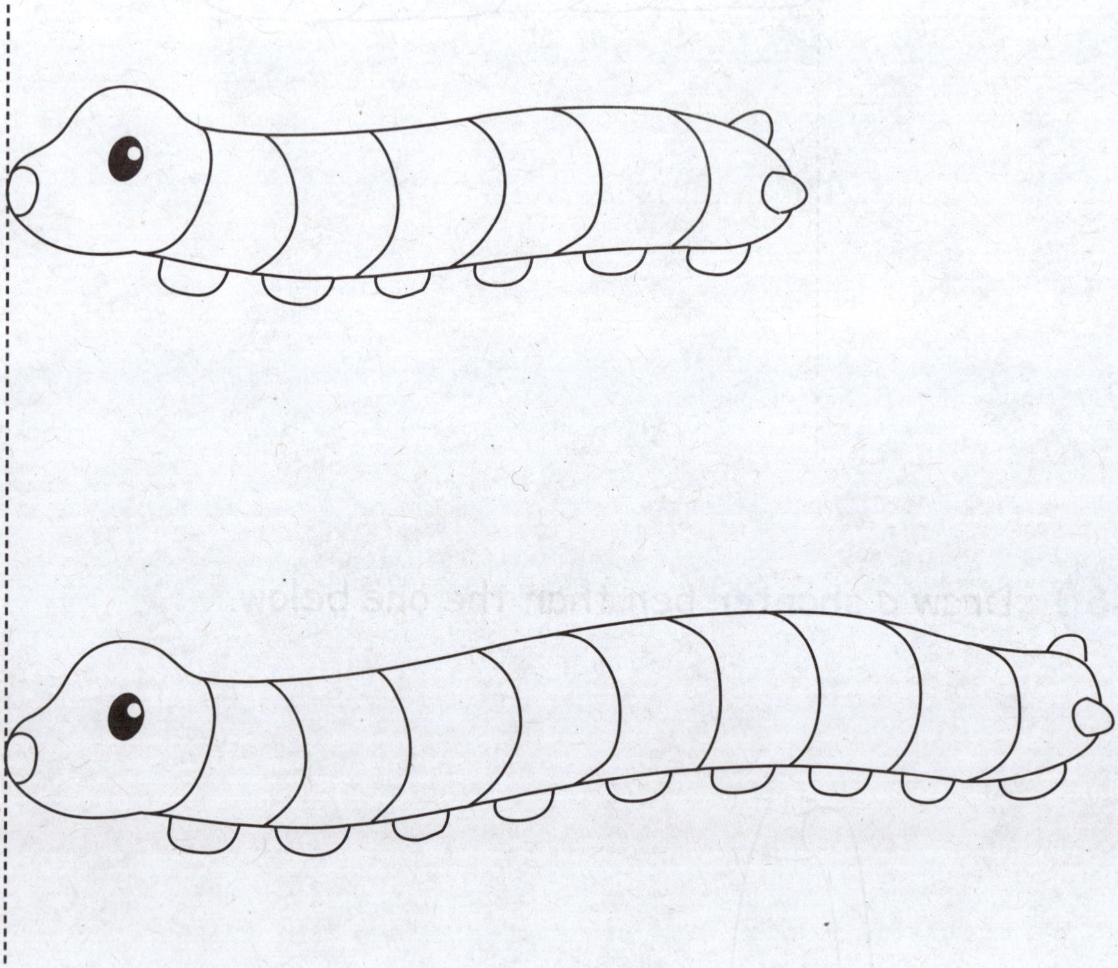

Learning Objective

Understanding length

8 Colour the **shorter** snake red.
Colour the **longer** snake brown.

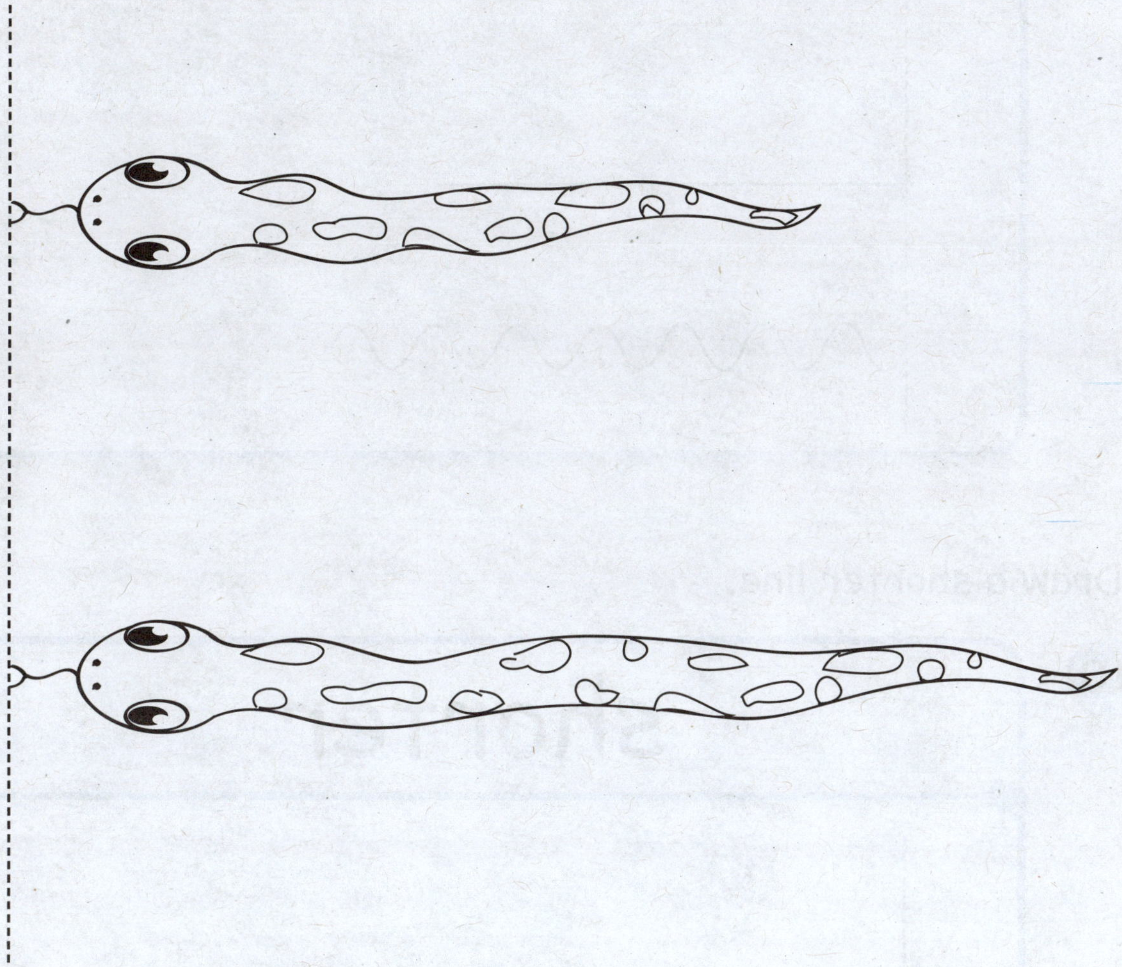

Learning Objective

Understanding length

Circle the correct line.

9

longer

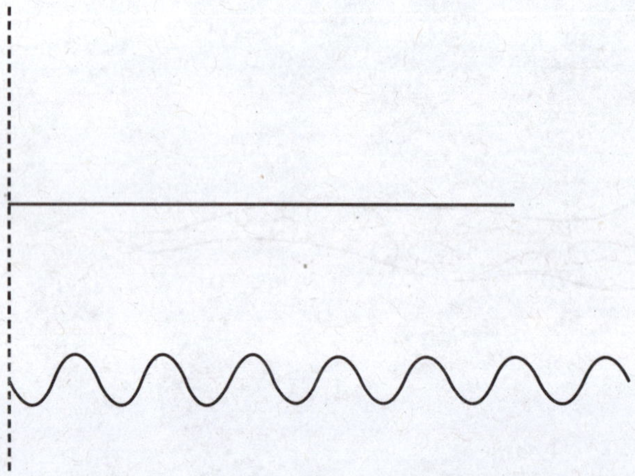

Draw a shorter line.

10

shorter

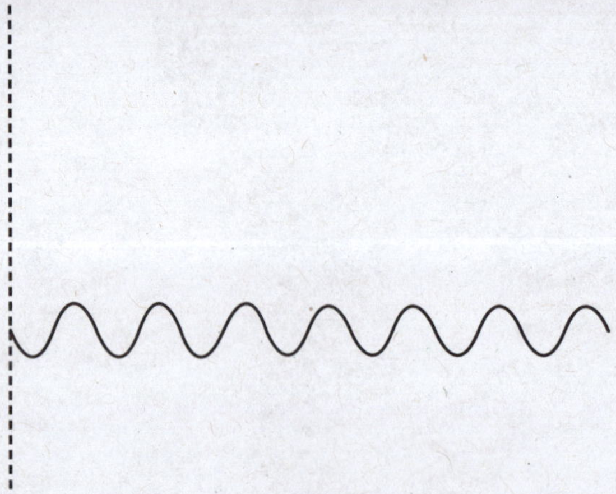

Learning Objective

Understanding length

ACTIVITY 30

Name ....

Class .... Date ....

/10 marks

1 Circle the **heavier** animal.

2 Circle the **lighter** fruit.

Learning Objective

Introducing weight

3 Colour the **heavier** fruit.

4 Colour the **lighter** object.

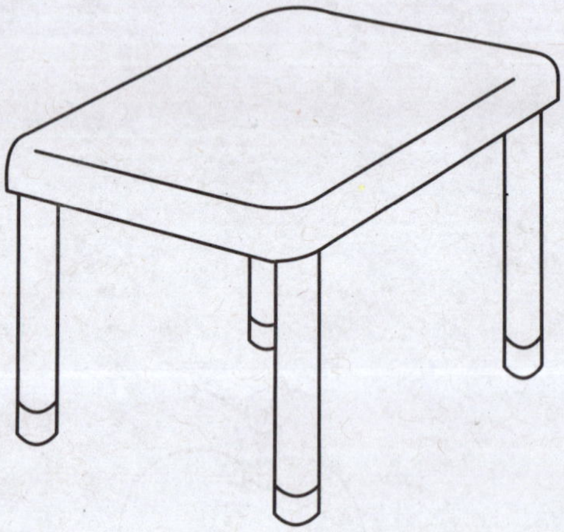

Learning Objective

Introducing weight

5 Colour the **heavier** fruit.

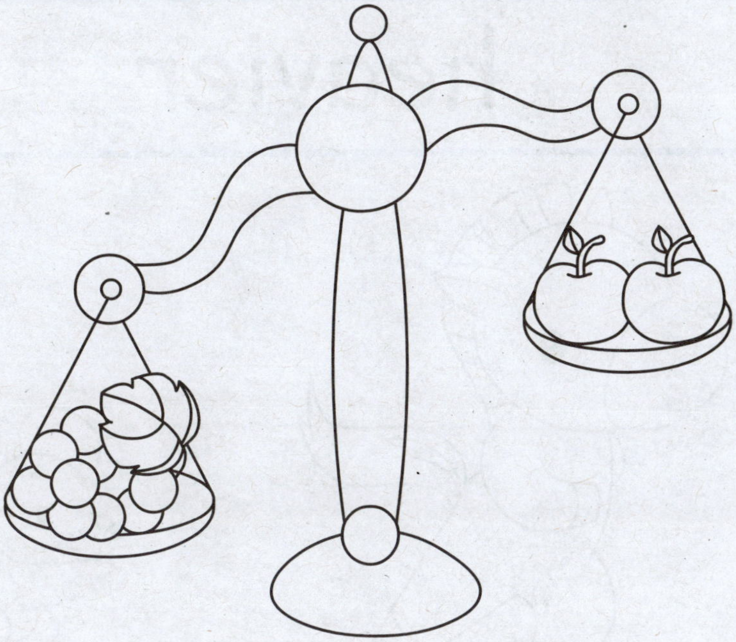

6 Circle the **lighter** animal.

Learning Objective

Introducing weight

Circle the correct object.

7

heavier

8

lighter

Learning Objective

Introducing weight

9 Which jug is **full**? Circle it.

Learning Objective

Introducing weight

10 Which jug is **empty**? Circle it.

Learning Objective

Introducing weight

ACTIVITY 31

Name ....

Class .... Date ....

/5 marks

1 Colour the jug with **more** water.

2 Colour the vase with **less** water.

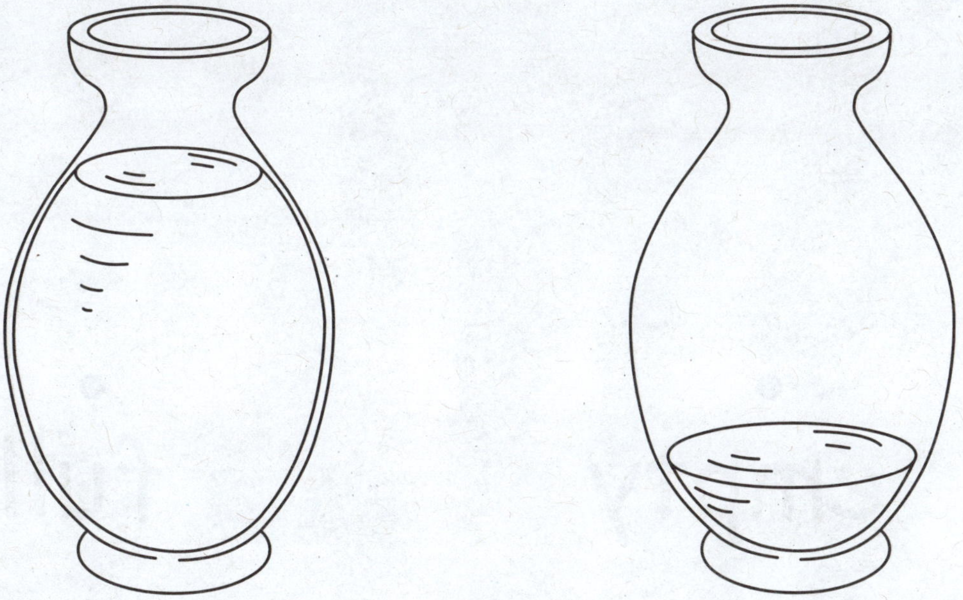

Learning Objective

Exploring volume

3 Match the words to the correct pictures.

empty

full

Learning Objective

Exploring volume

4 Draw on the glass **A** to show **more** water than glass **B**.

Learning Objective

Exploring volume

5 Draw on the glass **A** to show less water than glass **B**.

Learning Objective

Exploring volume

ACTIVITY 32

Name ....

Class .... Date ....

/23 marks

Circle the **bigger** number in each set.

1	3	4	
2	0	2	
3	9	7	
4	2	8	
5	5	7	
6	3	6	
7	6	8	
8	0	5	

Learning Objective

Comparing numbers

Circle the **smaller** number in each set.

9	1	4
10	10	2
11	8	7
12	2	3
13	5	4
14	3	9
15	0	1
16	8	5

Learning Objective

Comparing numbers

Circle the correct number.

17	bigger number	6	10
18	smaller number	4	2
19	smaller number	7	9

Learning Objective

Comparing numbers

Circle the correct number.

20

bigger number	3	1

21

bigger number	5	8

22

smaller number	4	9

23

bigger number	2	7

Learning Objective

Comparing numbers

ACTIVITY 33

Name ....

Class .... Date ....

/12 marks

Which set is smaller, A or B? Count and circle the smaller set.

1
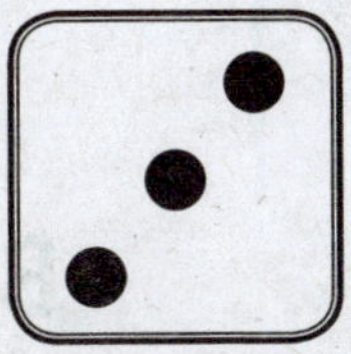
A
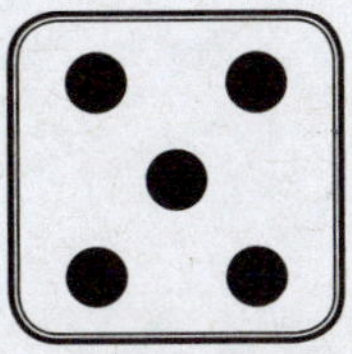
B

2
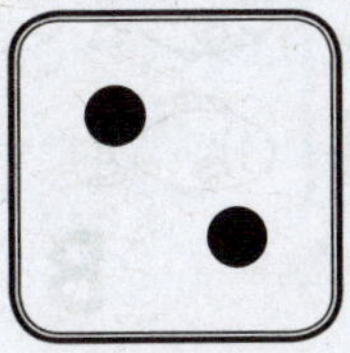
A
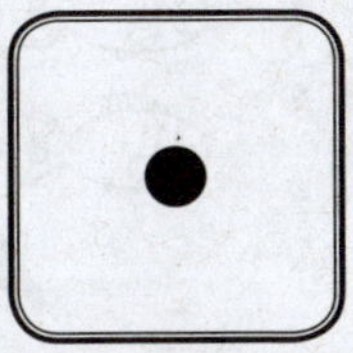
B

3
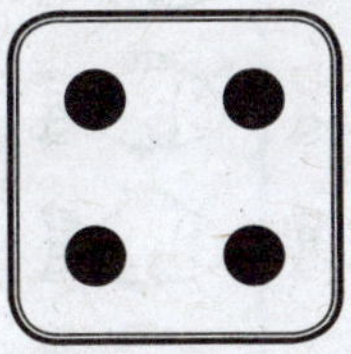
A
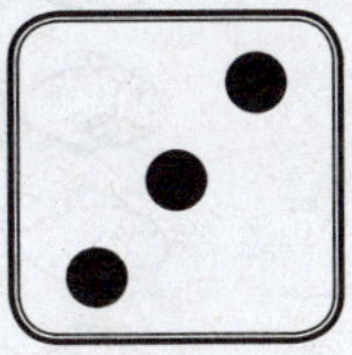
B

4
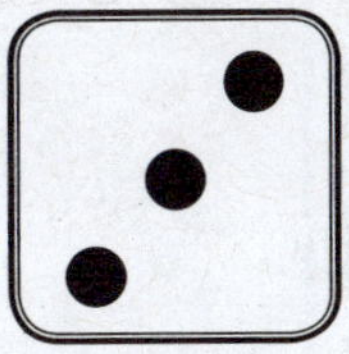
A
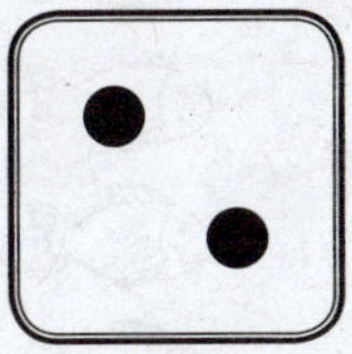
B

5
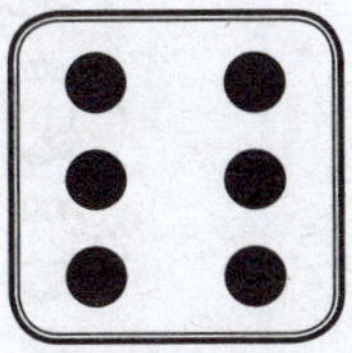
A

B

6

A
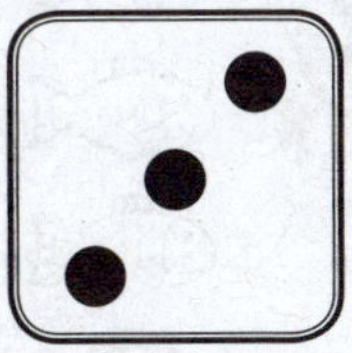
B

Learning Objective

Comparing numbers

Which set is **bigger**, A or B? Count and circle the **bigger** set.

7

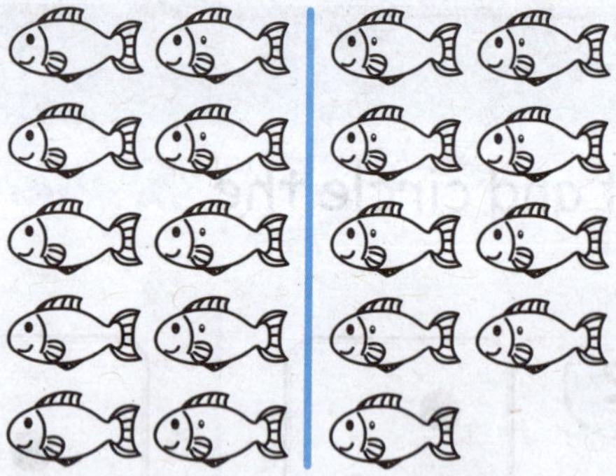

A B

8

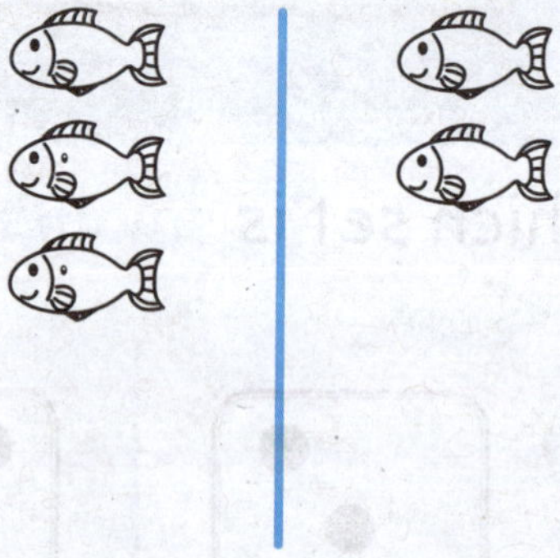

A B

9

A B

10

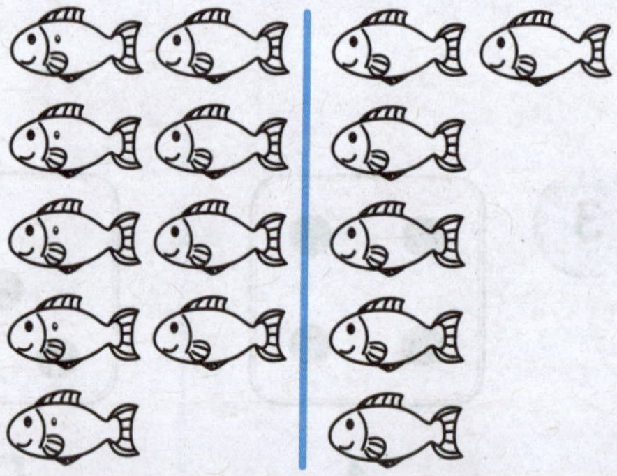

A B

11

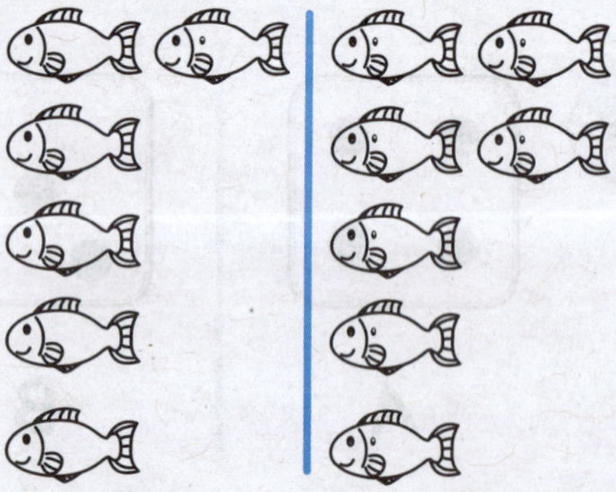

A B

12

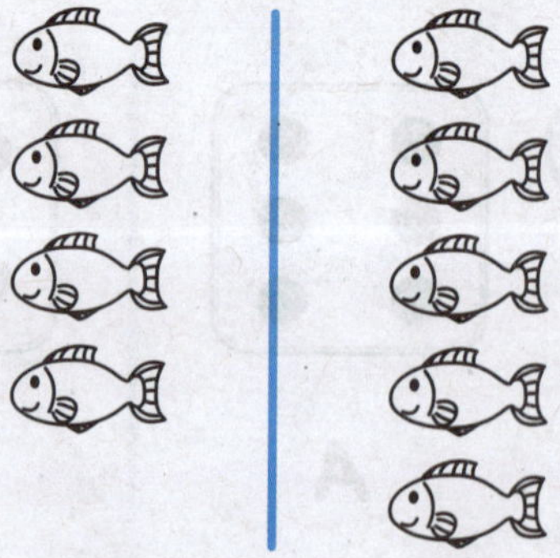

A B

Learning Objective

Comparing numbers

Activity 34

Name ....

Class .... Date ....

/10 marks

Circle the **longer** pencil in each set.

1

2

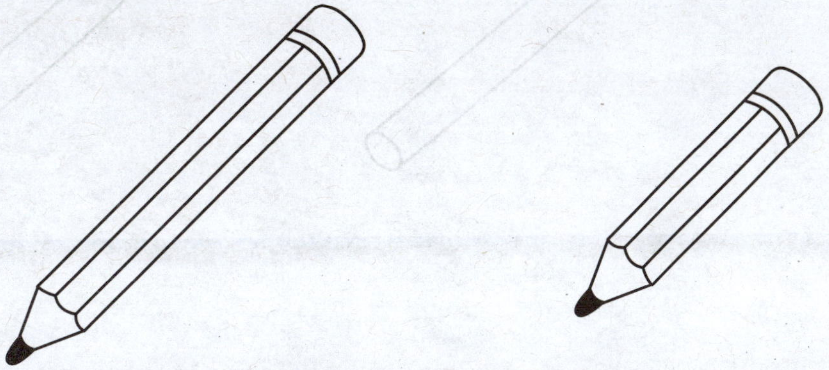

Learning Objective

Comparing length

Circle the shorter stick in each set.

3

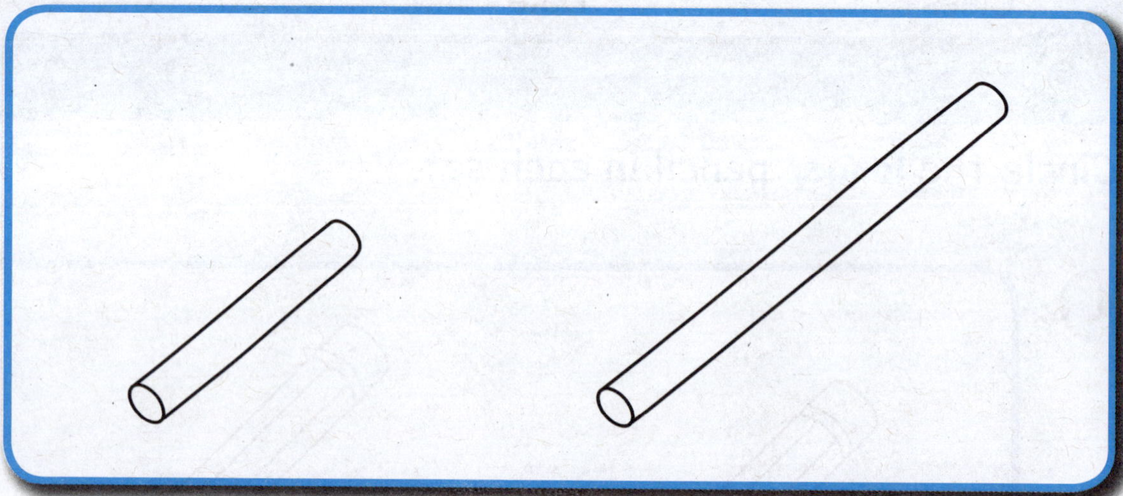

4

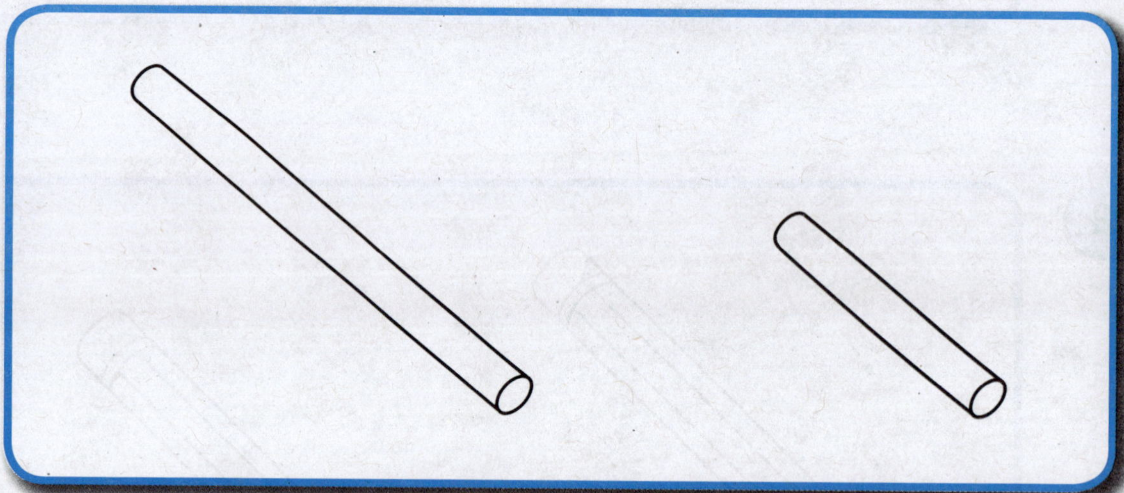

Learning Objective

Comparing length

Colour the longer ruler in each set.

5

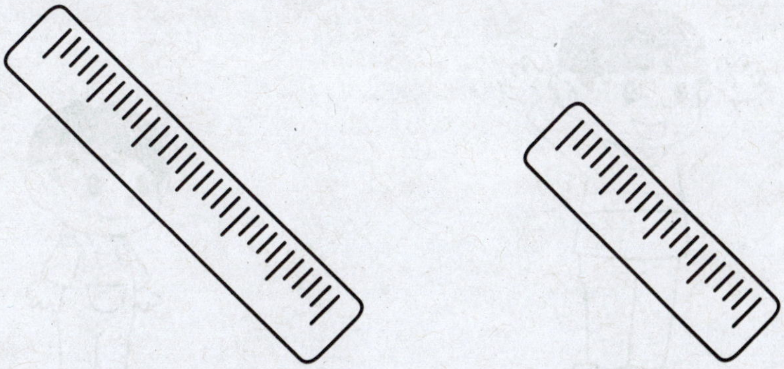

6

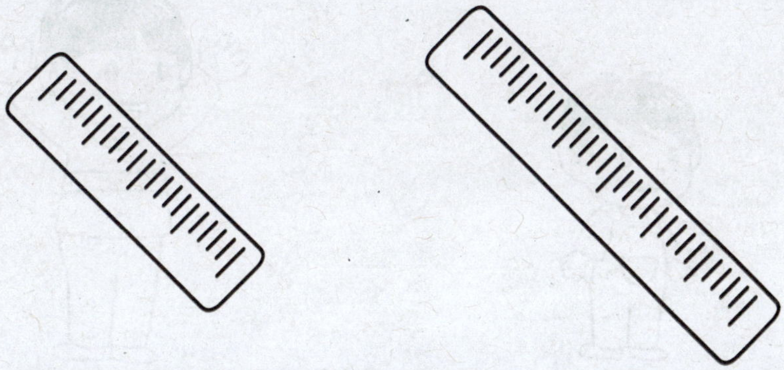

7

Learning Objective

Comparing length

Circle the **shorter** child in each set.

8

9

10

Learning Objective

Comparing length

ACTIVITY 35

Name ....

Class .... Date ....

/18 marks

Colour the **bigger** animal in each set.

1

elephant

rat

2

giraffe

cat

3

bird

hippopotamus

Learning Objective

Comparing size, weight and volume

Colour the **smaller** fruit in each set.

4

watermelon

apple

5

orange

durian

6

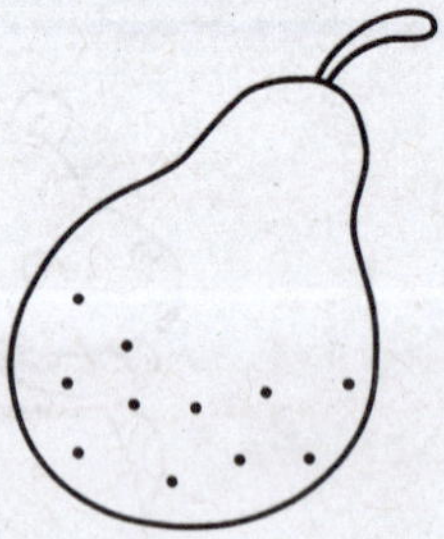

pear

cherry

Learning Objective

Comparing size, weight and volume

Circle the jug that has **more** water in each set.

7

8

9

Learning Objective

Comparing size, weight and volume

Colour the **empty** container in each set.

10

11

12

Learning Objective

Comparing size, weight and volume

Circle the **heavier** group in each set.

13

14

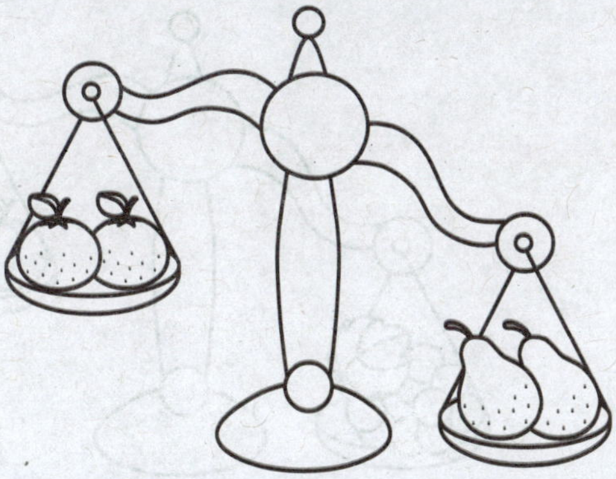

15

Learning Objective

Comparing size, weight and volume

Colour the lighter group in each set.

16

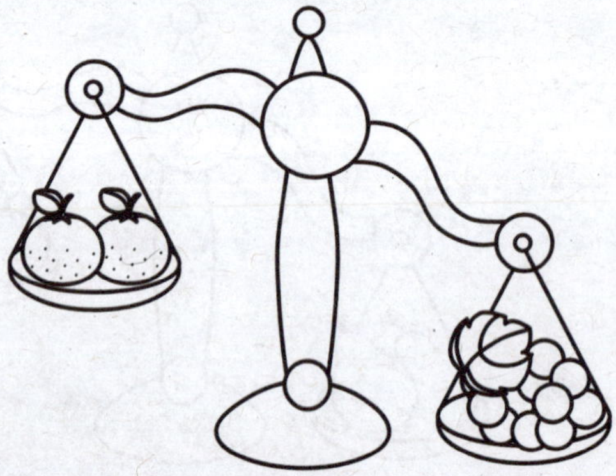

17

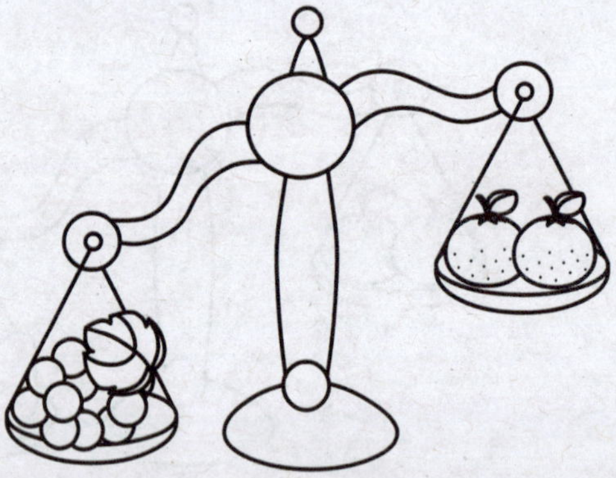

18

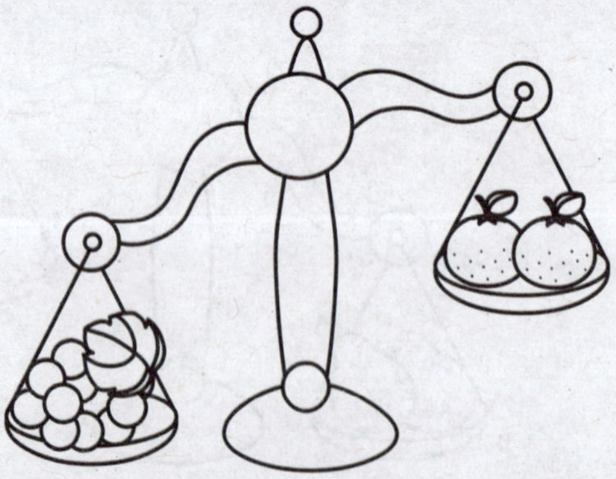

Learning Objective

Comparing size, weight and volume

ACTIVITY 36

Name .... Date ....

Class ....

/8 marks

1 Draw lines and put the shapes into 2 different groups.

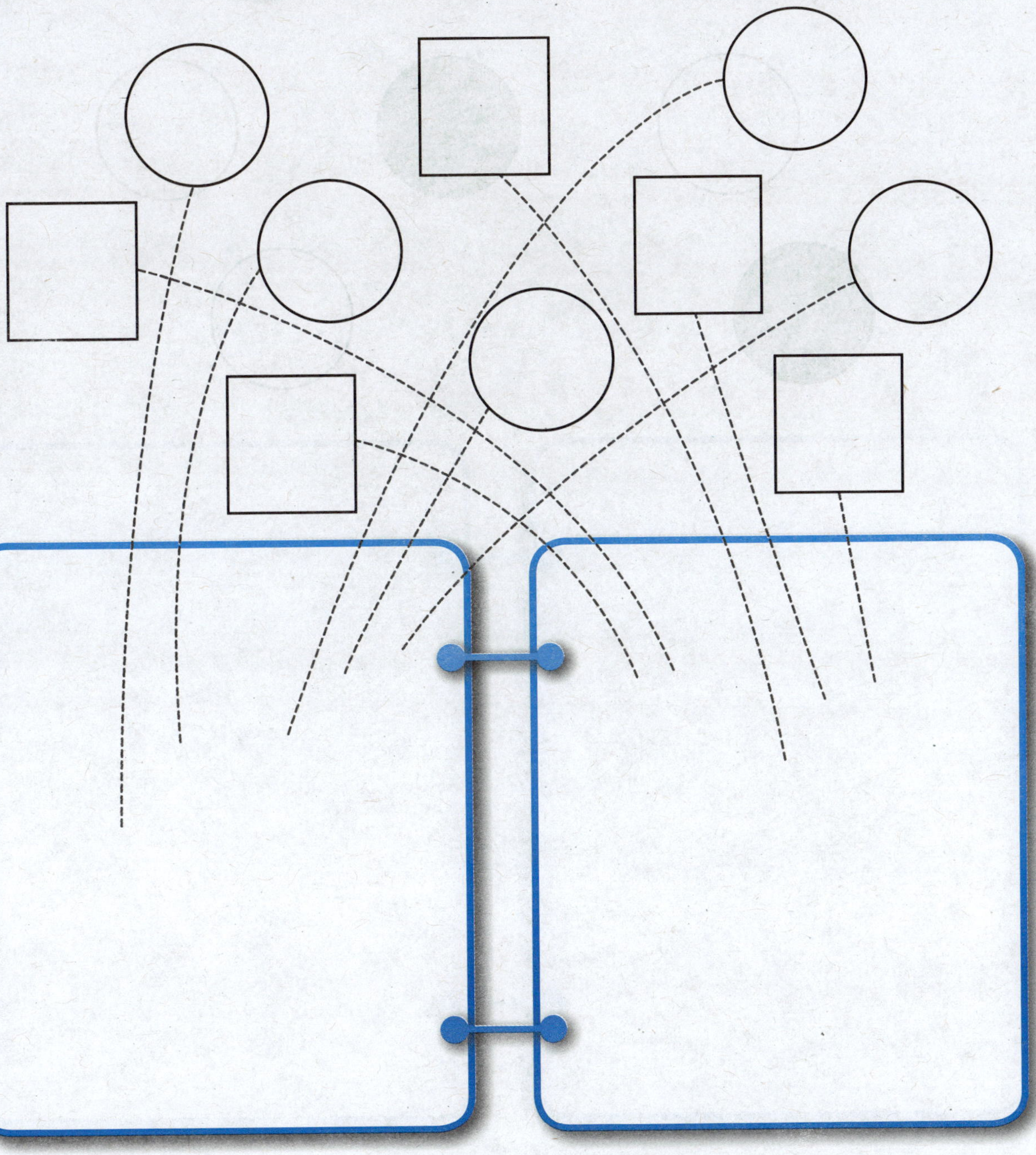

Learning Objective

Classifying things

2 Draw lines and put the circles into 2 different groups.

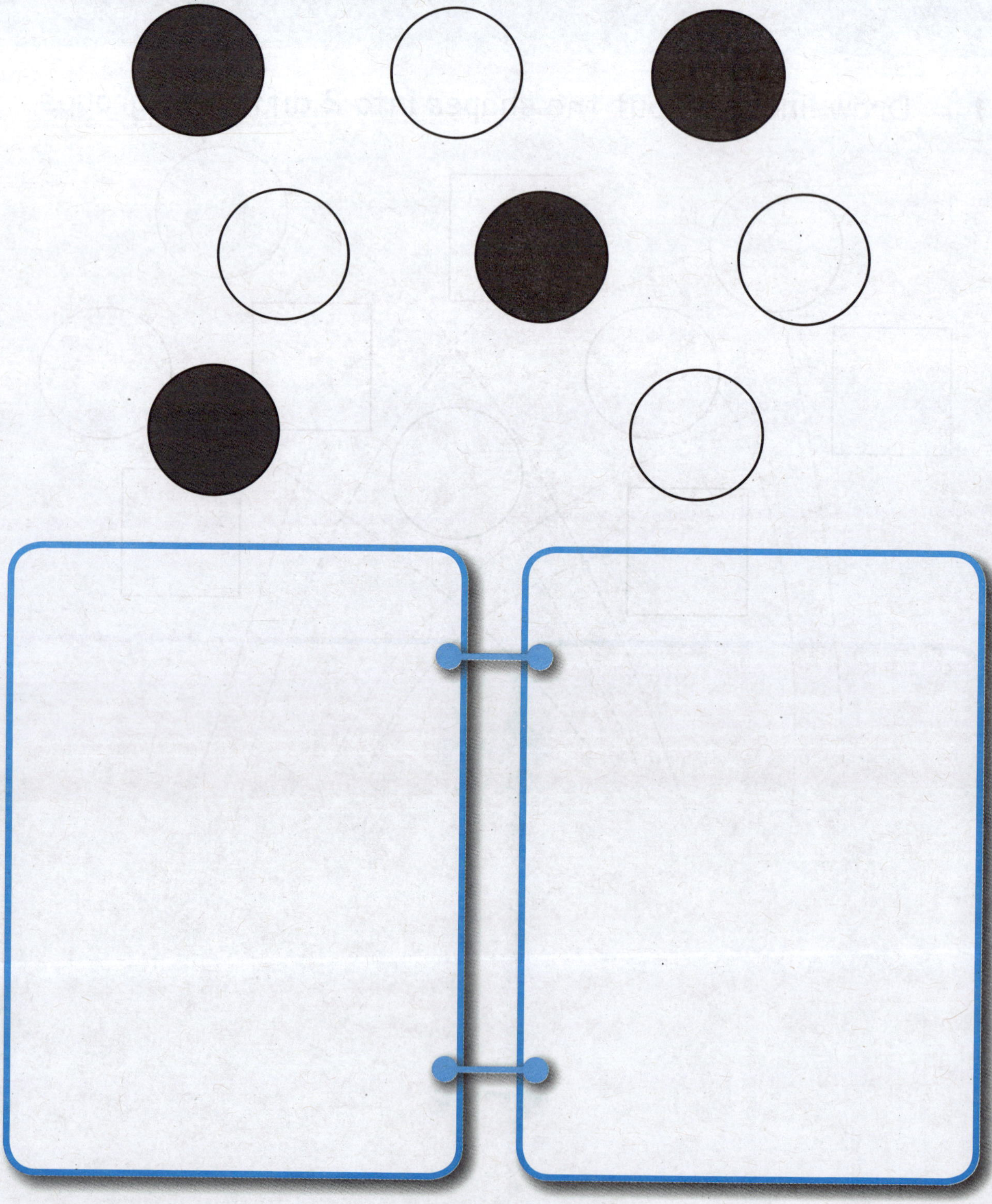

Learning Objective

Classifying things

3 Draw lines and put the shapes into 2 different groups.

Learning Objective

Classifying things

4 Draw lines and put the shapes into 2 different groups.

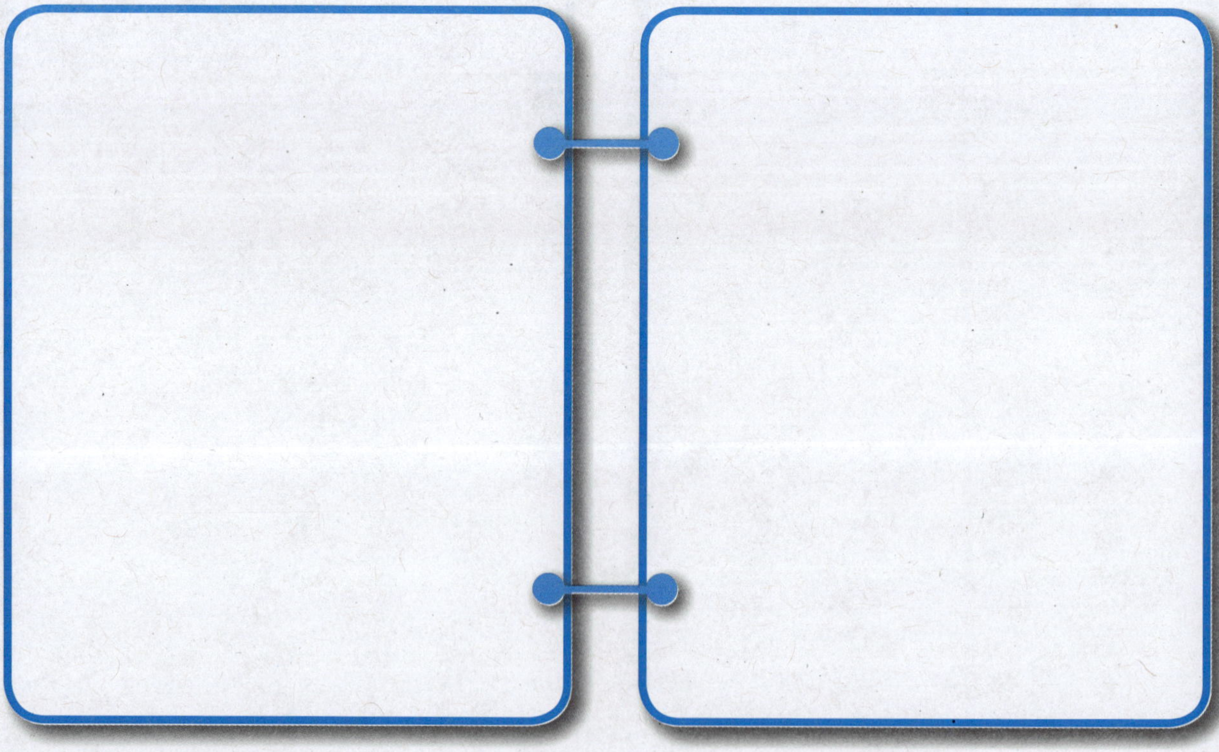

5 Draw lines and put the fruit into 2 different groups.

watermelon

orange

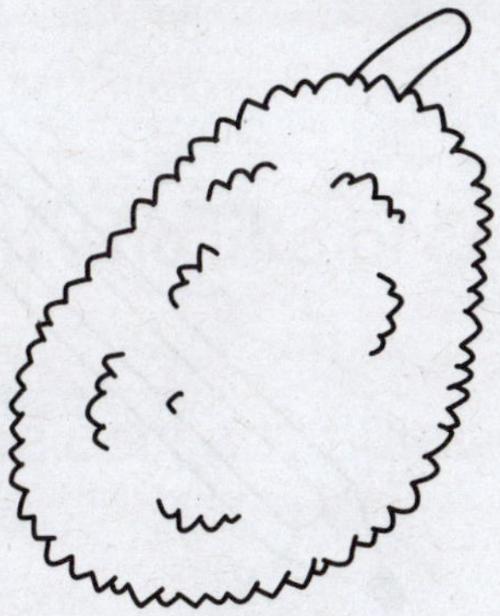

jackfruit

apple

durian

cherry

Learning Objective

Classifying things

6 Draw lines and put the objects into 2 different groups.

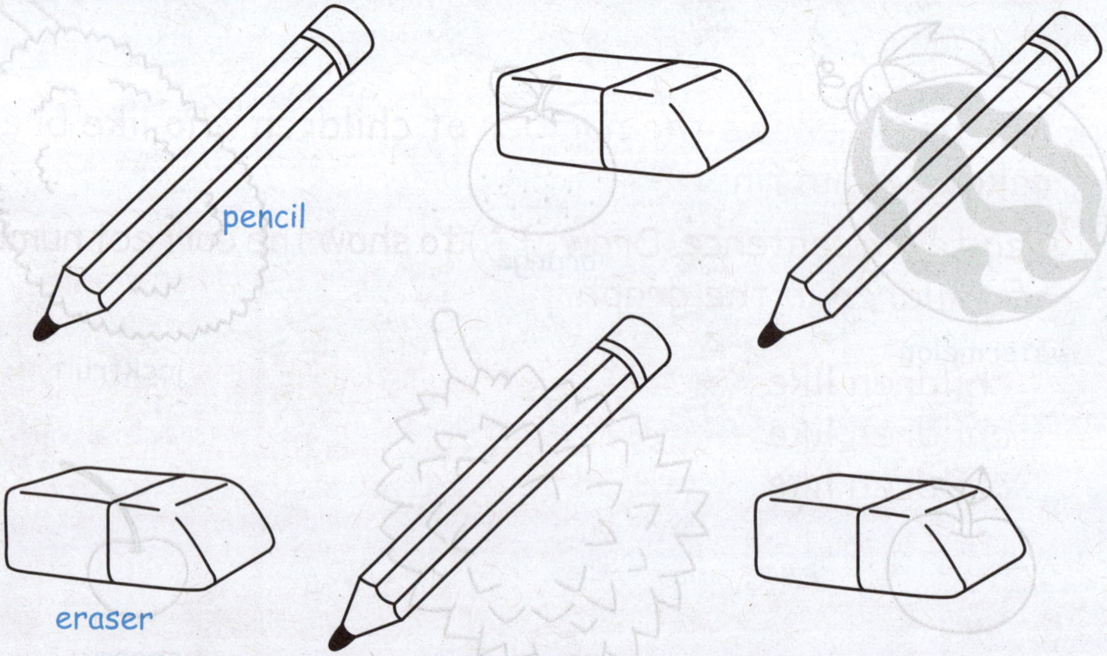

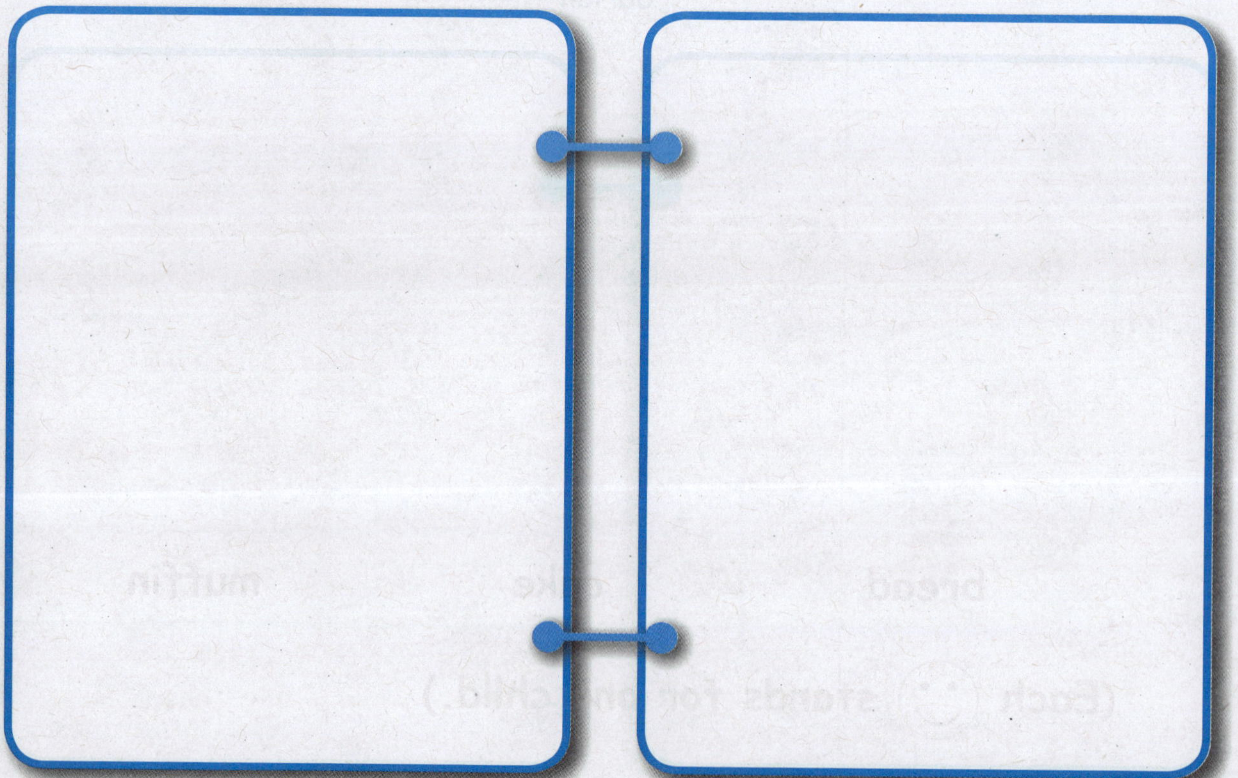

Learning Objective

Classifying things

7 Draw lines and put the objects into 2 different groups.

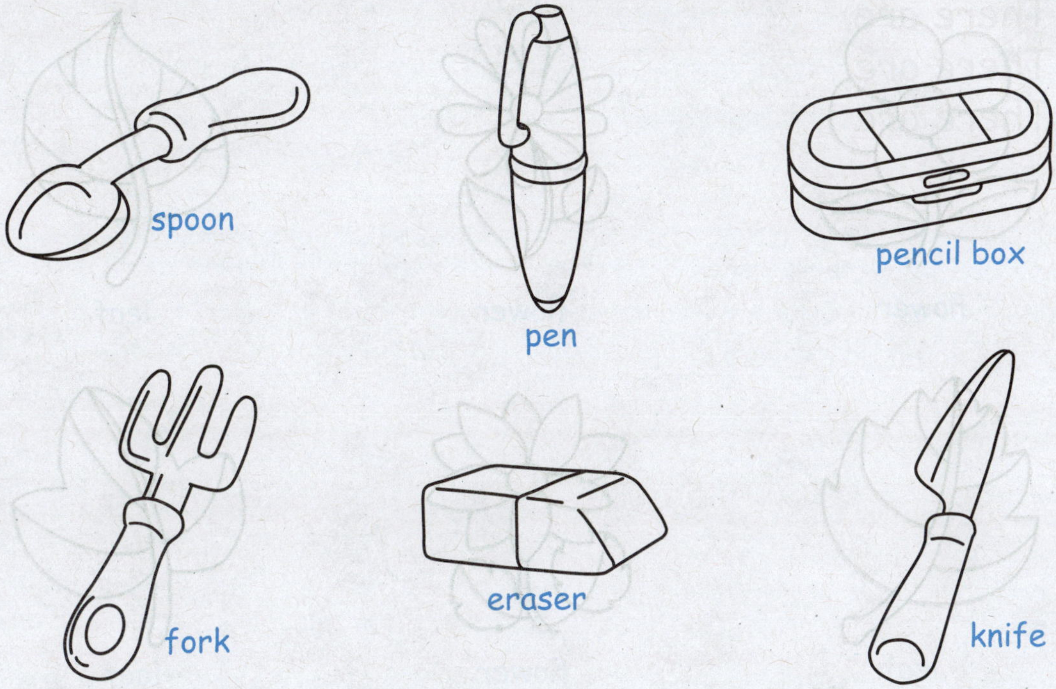

Learning Objective

Classifying things

8 Draw lines and put the objects into 2 different groups.

flower

flower

leaf

leaf

flower

leaf

Learning Objective

Classifying things

ACTIVITY 37

Name ....

Class .... Date ....

/6 marks

1 Count and trace the missing bottles.

5 bottles

Learning Objective

Presenting and interpreting information using pictures

2 Count and trace the missing flowers.

6 flowers

Learning Objective

Presenting and interpreting information using pictures

3 Count and trace the missing trees.

7 trees

Learning Objective

Presenting and interpreting information using pictures

4 Draw the missing squares.

8 squares

Learning Objective

Presenting and interpreting information using pictures

5 Draw the missing circles.

9 circles

6 Count and draw the missing fish.

10 fish

Learning Objective

Presenting and interpreting information using pictures

ACTIVITY 38

Name ....

Class .... Date ....

/7 marks

Look at the picture graph. Fill in the correct numbers.

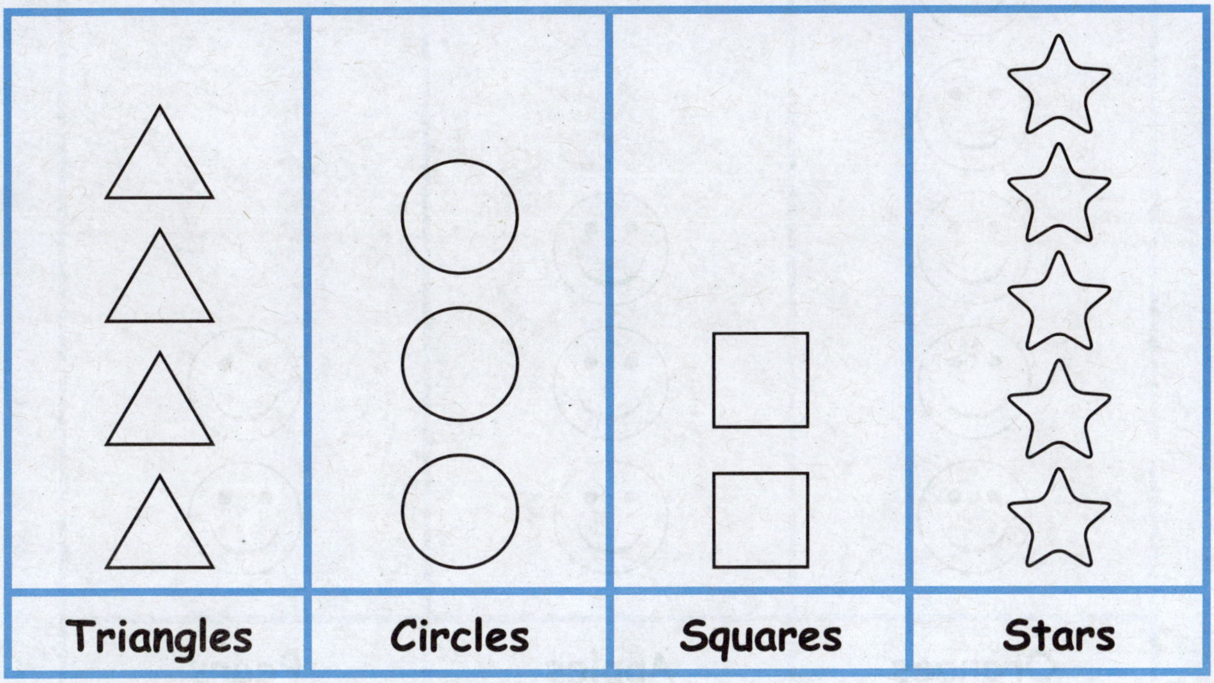

1 There are ________ 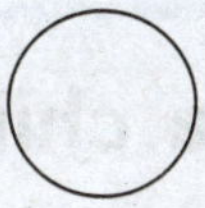 .

2 There are ________  .

3 There are ________ 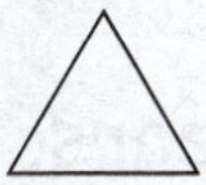 .

4 There are ________  .

Learning Objective

Counting objects in picture graphs

Look at the picture graph. Fill in the correct numbers.

Favourite Fruit

(Each ☺ stands for one child.)

5 ________ children like apples.

6 ________ children like pears.

7 ________ children like oranges.

Learning Objective

Counting objects in picture graphs

ACTIVITY 39

Name .... Class .... Date ....

/16 marks

Read the sentences. Draw the correct number of shapes.

1 There are 4 rectangles.
There is 1 oval.

Rectangle	**Oval**

Learning Objective
Completing picture graphs

Read the sentences. Draw the correct number of shapes.

2 There are 4 triangles.
There are 2 circles.
There are 5 squares.

Square	**Circle**	**Triangle**

Learning Objective

Completing picture graphs

Activity 40

Name ....

Class .... Date ....

/26 marks

1 The graph shows the number of children who like bread, cake and muffin.

Read each sentence. Draw to show the correct number of children in the graph.

4 children like **muffin**.
3 children like **bread**.
5 children like **cake**.

bread	**cake**	**muffin**

(Each stands for one child.)

Learning Objective

Using symbols to represent numbers

2) The graph shows the number of children who like drawing, reading and singing.

Read each sentence. Draw to show the correct number of children in the graph.

5 children like singing.
3 children like drawing.
6 children like reading.

reading	**drawing**	**singing**

(Each stands for one child.)

Learning Objective

Using symbols to represent numbers

ACTIVITY 41

Name ....

Class .... Date ....

/13 marks

1 Do you know the parts of the clock?
Colour the clock.

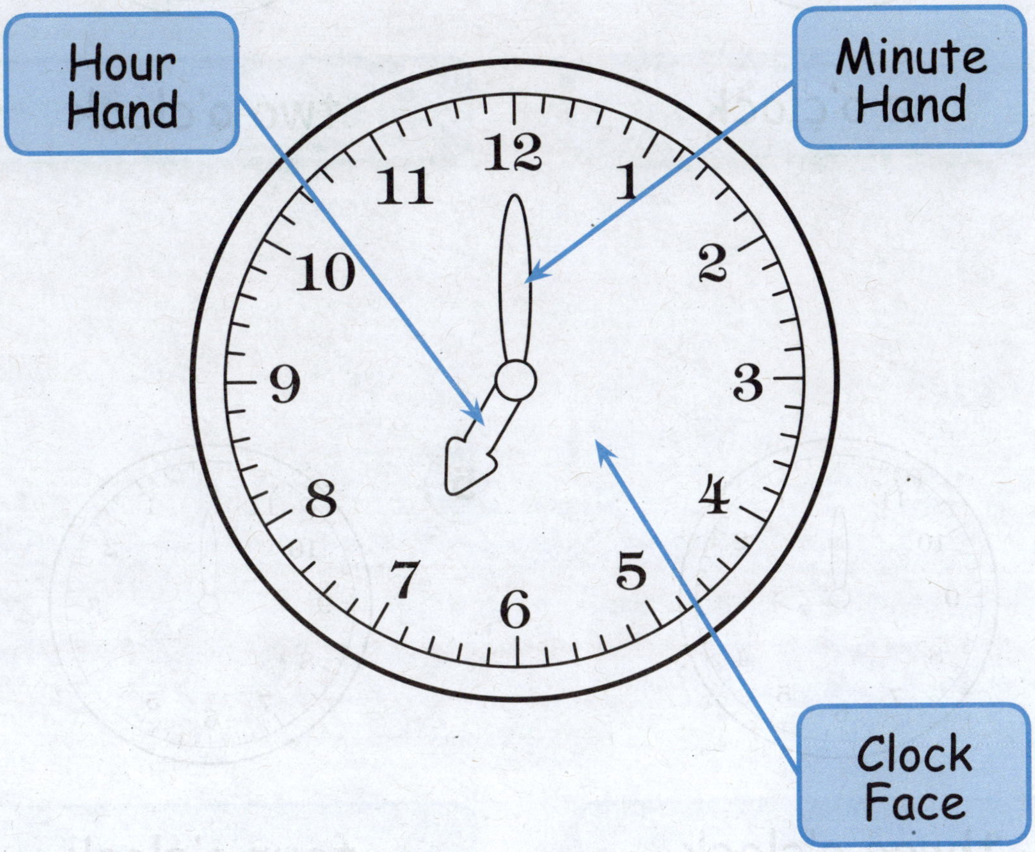

Learning Objective

Telling Time

What time is it?

Trace and colour all the hour hands.

2

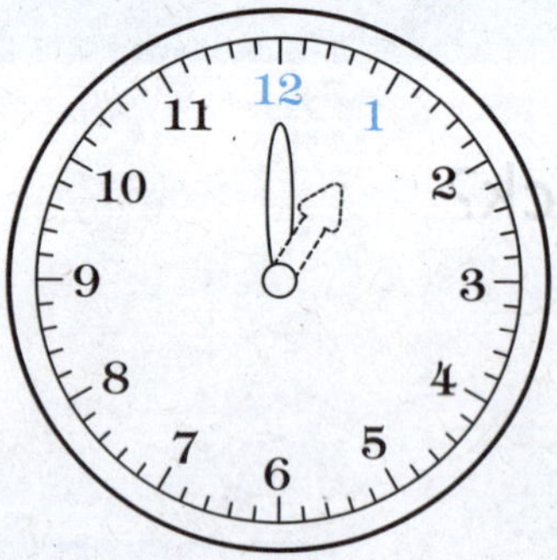

one o'clock

3

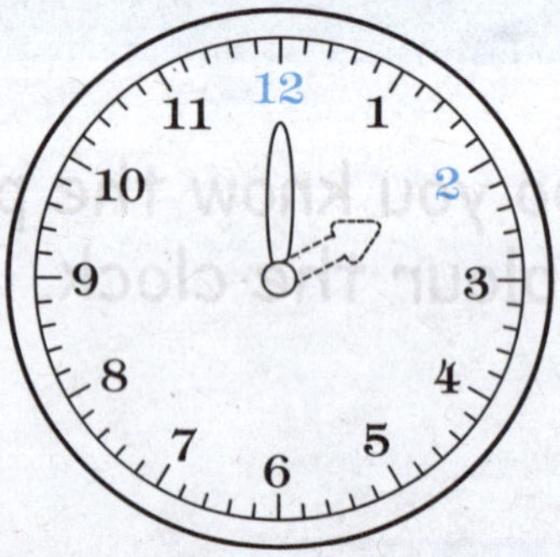

two o'clock

4

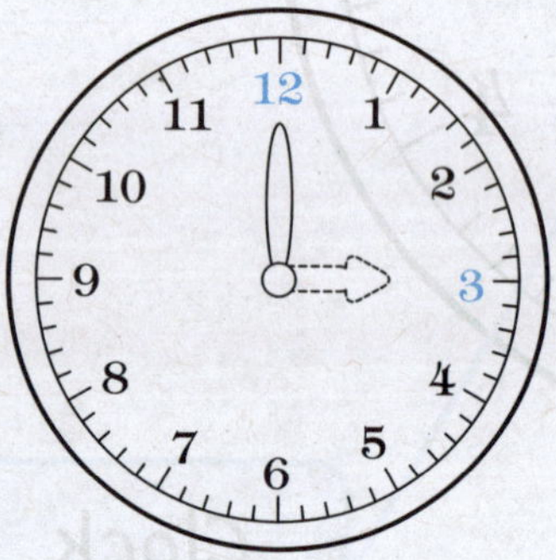

three o'clock

5

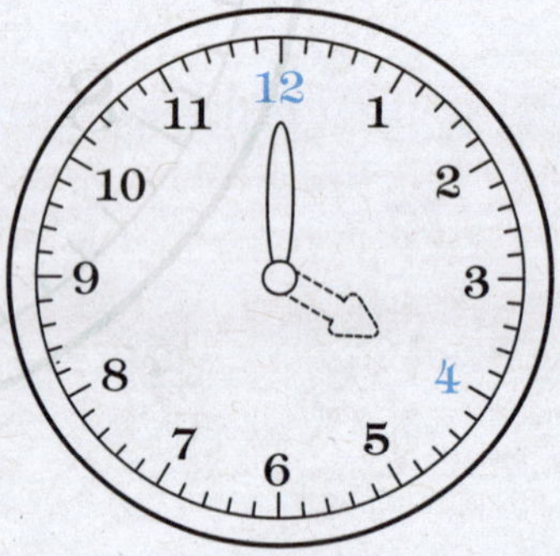

four o'clock

Learning Objective

Telling Time

What time is it?
Trace and colour all the hour hands.

6

five o'clock

7

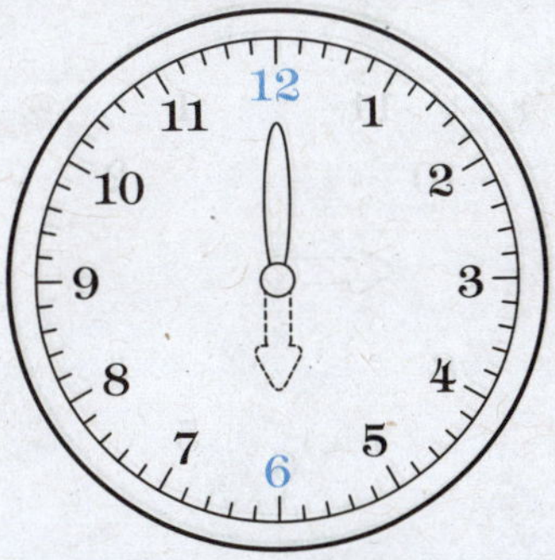

six o'clock

8

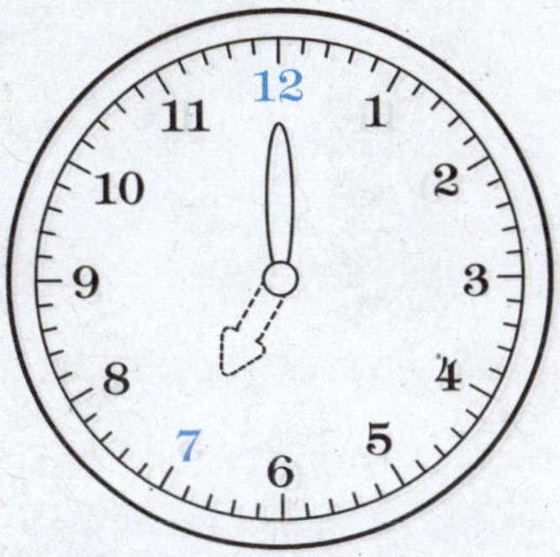

seven o'clock

9

eight o'clock

Learning Objective
Telling Time

What time is it?
Trace and colour all the hour hands.

10

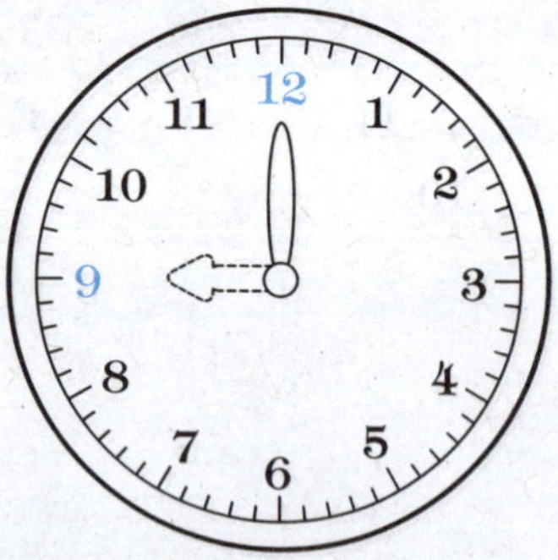

nine o'clock

11

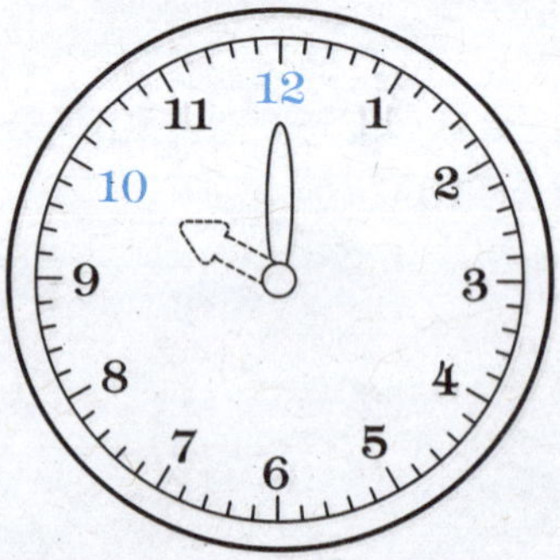

ten o'clock

12

eleven o'clock

13

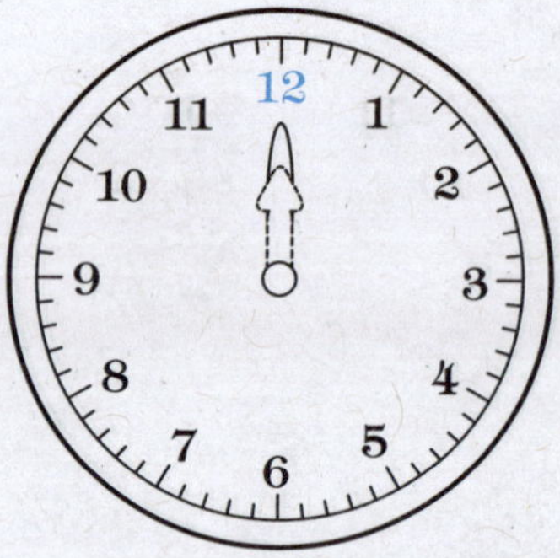

twelve o'clock

Learning Objective

Telling Time

ACTIVITY 42

Name .... Class .... Date ....

/2 marks

1 This is what Peter does in the morning.
Colour the hour and minute hands on the clocks.
Write the correct time.

7 o'clock

Peter wakes up.

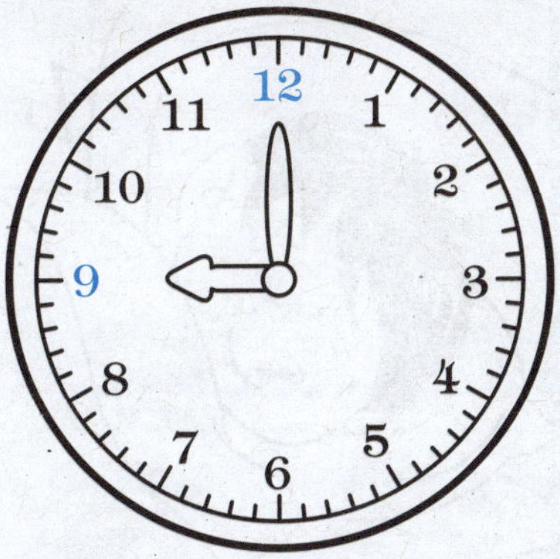

o'clock

Peter eats his breakfast.

Learning Objective

Telling Time

2 This is what Peter does at night.
Colour the hour and minute hands on the clocks.
Write the correct time.

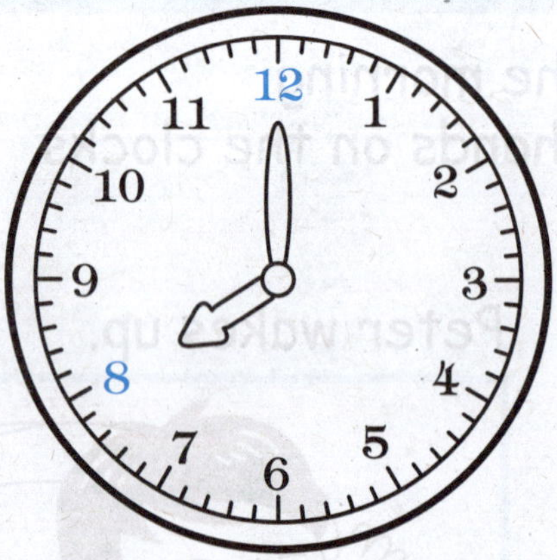

[ ] o'clock

Peter watches cartoons.

[ ] o'clock

Peter goes to bed.

ACTIVITY 43

Name .... Class .... Date ....

/4 marks

Write the time using o'clock.

1

2 o'clock

2

o'clock

Learning Objective

Telling the time using o'clock

Write the time using o'clock.

3

☐ o'clock

4

☐ o'clock

Learning Objective

Telling the time using o'clock

ACTIVITY 44

Name .... Class .... Date ....

/4 marks

Fill in the blanks with **morning** or **night**.

Peter goes to school.

1) 10 o'clock in the ______.

Learning Objective

Understanding time in the morning and at night

Fill in the blanks with morning or night.

Peter has dinner.

2 7 o'clock at ________.

Learning Objective

Understanding time in the morning and at night

Fill in the blanks with **morning** or **night**.

John wears his uniform.

3 9 o'clock in the ______.

Learning Objective

Understanding time in the morning and at night

Fill in the blanks with **morning** or **night**.

John sleeps.

4 10 o'clock at ________.